AMMA

AMMA

Saraid de Silva

WEATHERGLASS BOOKS

For Gran.

Family

Josephina (Amma/Gran)

|

Sithara (Mum)

|

Annie

I never eat sensibly when you're away.
I make do with odd scraps of food
that don't need heating up,
or nibble on a biscuit or two.

Absence, Alistair Te Ariki Campbell

Annie
2018, London

Annie Ano Fernando doesn't care much for men.

Her grandfather died before she was born. She says her father is dead, though this is a lie. Sometimes she is attracted to men, but it usually fades when she hears them speak. Only one man has ever really mattered. In three stops she will arrive at his doorstep.

The streets here are swollen with people. She has overheard Arabic, Spanish and French since stepping off the plane. There are more South Asians than she has ever seen in her life. She has already imprinted on every grandmother that looks a little like hers.

Annie has to check herself to stop gaping. It is painful, so pathetically Christchurch of her to be in awe of London. She just can't grasp the scale. As soon as she disembarked she was funnelled into the underground, the space between her armpit and shirt growing warmer and wetter the closer she got to the city.

1

Then she had heaved herself onto the platform of a windowless train station. The escalator marched its passengers to the top, shedding one after another, and she wondered if she should give herself up to something so relentless. At last she was shot out into the middle of a city where no one knew her or cared. Outside the station she runs into a dairy for a bottle of water and stares at the wall of alcohol. Rows of beers and RTDs. People push past her to buy their chewing gum and energy drinks. Everyone is in the middle of something. She tries to imagine what it would take to be somebody here.

At five foot four, Annie is by far the tallest woman in her family. Her ears stick straight out from the sides of her head, poking through the hair she uses to cover them. Her gaze is so direct it makes people uneasy. As a child, unnerving people made her feel like a freak. As an adult, she enjoys it. Her face has none of the poetry of her gran's, nor the startling drama of her mum's. But on a good day Annie knows she is cute.

Today is not a good day. Her eyes are puffy from crying. Leaving Gran this time felt like leaving her whole life.

Eleven hours in the air sucked every drop of moisture from Annie's skin. Her hair is slick, like someone ran a wide-toothed comb smeared with gel through the top and pasted her roots to her scalp.

Annie has just spent two weeks in Melbourne with Gran, Maude Aunty, Vida Aunty and Nathan Uncle. Technically they are her second cousins. Vida Aunty is her grandfather's sister Maude's daughter and Nathan Uncle is her husband. Gran lives in a small cottage in their garden, same as she did in Hamilton with Annie and her mother, but happier. Maude and Gran laugh like witches late into the night.

On the aeroplane she had wished she was eight again, sitting in a bath with Gran singing 'Istanbul (not Constanti-nople)' and pouring perfectly warm water down Annie's back. It was probably the last time she felt safe. Gran knew Annie was going to London, but she did not ask who she would be visiting. Nervous, Annie offered up a lie anyway, and said her first weeks here would be spent on the couch of a friend from uni.

There is no real viewing of the place, no skyline to stare at. The houses she passes on the bus switch from mansion to crumbling apartment block and back again in the space of a few hundred metres. Someone her age sits opposite her. They're East Asian, platinum-blonde hair. The tattoos across their arms look like faded runes. Annie presses the bell for her stop and makes eye contact. Someone looking this gay and this hot on a bus at this time in the morning doesn't seem fair. She watches them take in her muscled shoulders and brand-new suitcase. They smile and toy with a beaded necklace.

Annie wobbles out a smile in return. She hopes her teeth don't look as furry as they feel. She thinks about starting a conversation. Perhaps she could say that England is just as cloudy as she heard it was. Roll her eyes and shrug. Would that make them laugh? She wraps her fingers around the handles of her suitcase, wets her lips and then stops herself. Her first words to this Londoner can't be about the *weather*. Annie gets off without saying anything, lifting her belongings like they are weightless and swinging them behind her. The suitcase wheels thrum on the pavement like a heartbeat.

Annie finds his street following the instructions she copied into a notebook, knowing her phone battery would not last. It's nice, maybe nicer than she expected. Wide, with cute brick houses and plenty of greenery.

De Beauvoir Town. Annie could live here. She could get a house big enough for her and Gran. They would buy food from different stores like rich people − meat from the butcher, bread from the bakery, cheese from the cheesemonger. The only thing standing between her and a life here is a shit ton of money.

This address is one she stole, found etched in jerky pencil on the back of a prayer card in Gran's cottage, hidden under a pile of old magazines. It could have been rubbish waiting to be chucked, but Annie saw Gran wipe the magazines clean of dust and tuck the card between the same two issues. She darted back as soon as Gran was asleep and studied it.

His name, Suri Fernando, a phone number and an address. She had to squint to make out the postcode around the words of the Hail Mary.

Number 49. It's big, two storey. A pretty wrought-iron gate. Annie's free hand trembles. She typed his number into her phone many times but never had the balls to follow through with a call or even a message. It's likely he's not home. He could be working, out of town, out of the country even.

'Alright then,' she says aloud. She has come so far.

She walks up the steps and knocks on the door, then skitters back down where she feels safer. Istanbul. Constantinople. Annie hears footsteps growing closer and waits, holding her breath. In her dreams she has stood in front of this door many times.

A man who is skinny and dark like her mum opens it, blinking across at her. He is wearing shorts and a blue t-shirt that says 'Ran London Marathon'. His hairy calves taper into ankles so delicate and familiar that Annie's eyes fill with tears.

He doesn't look angry, which is a good start. He wears glasses with thick brown two-tone frames. He's so stylish, with his nicely manicured beard, that it throws Annie. He takes in her cheap luggage, her trackpants, her old, sweat-stained tank. Annie squirms, mentally punishing herself for not being cool enough for London, but she doesn't look away.

He opens his mouth to talk and stops, gaze darting past her as if to check whether she is alone. When he sees that she is, he winces. Annie's tears trickle down over her lip.

I'm your niece, she says.

Suri nods a yes and massages his beard.

Hi, Suri Uncle, she says, testing it out.

To Annie's relief he smiles. It's a good smile, the sort that polishes a face.

Annie has to stifle a laugh. Somehow Suri, her mum's closest living relative, is bald.

Sithara

Maria Louisa Sithara Fernando sits on the floor of her bedroom getting ready for school. It is seven on a frozen morning in July. Her room is lit by one bulb on a stand with no lampshade. Her hair, long enough to kiss her waist, is dead.

Back home in Colombo, her hair was alive. It floated outwards as though underwater when she was sad, unfurling soft around her face. Sometimes it said the things that she could not. Her hair reached out to her amma when they lay down after lunch, too full and too hot to do anything other than bask like lizards on the wooden seat they called a couch and watch the ceiling fan twist slowly above them. Things have changed since she got here. Her family, herself. Both have shrunk. And when Appa died, her hair gave up.

The sun has not yet risen. The edges of the sky are fading from black into ghostly blue. If she loses concentration when leaving the house on mornings like this, her school shoes will slip on the black ice like she has two little enemies on her feet, and she will have to windmill her arms to stay upright. That moment between success and failure is an eternity.

Sithara is all triangles. She has a skinny neck and a pointed, almost hooked chin. Long eyelashes interrupt the severity of her face, giving her a sweetness. She avoids her reflection in the mirror nowadays, scared that the longer she looks, the more likely it is she will see something two-dimensional, something empty.

A section on the other side of the road is home only to a few sheep fenced in with wire. They are missing this morning. She wonders if it is too cold even for sheep. Tiny scraps of plastic are stitched around the wire, bouncing in the wind.

She brushes and ties her hair like she always does for school, with a strong middle parting, weaving it into a plait. It shrugs itself into the elastic and hangs heavy between her shoulders, plain and unfeeling.

Invercargill is a small town that thinks it is a city, at the bottom of a country full of white people who think they live in England. Everyone on television and radio here speaks like the Queen. Sithara hasn't been anywhere else in New Zealand yet. She hopes it isn't all like this.

The three of them — Sithara, her amma Josephina and her brother Suri — live in a narrow red house in Clifton. They came six years ago with her appa. They were shocked into silence by their new home. The blood-red wood, the sharp skinny window frames, the way it leered at them.

Amma wore a jacket and a coat over a bright yellow sari. She stuck out on the dull street like a sunflower. They had no real winter clothes. Amma stuffed a pink sarong under a sun hat for warmth; it drooped out from the rim like big wilted petals. She let her suitcase fall to the footpath, pushed both hands deep into her sleeves and scowled.

Appa just looked at the empty roads, checked left and right as though he had missed something. His hair was like Sithara's used to be, an extension of his thoughts, breathing. He kept it long at the top, brushed back from his face in an elegant side parting. When he was happy his curls rustled together like leaves.

Appa loved to listen to Sithara recounting her dreams, and to Suri reading poems aloud. He laughed at himself so quickly. He was the only one who could turn Amma's moods around. It was like he freed her from herself. He was by far the friendliest of the lot of them, but because he was dark with a thick accent he made the white people wary.

Sithara and Suri stood still, as paralysed as their parents, waiting for a cue. Suri's chubby fingers held Sithara's tight. She had to make being here okay. She tried to think of something to make Suri smile but lost the words in surprise when she opened her mouth and saw her breath materialise in front of her. She reached out a hand, trying to touch the ghost of her thoughts.

Where are all the people? Appa said softly, as the strangeness of the place poured over them.

Sithara yells for Suri to get out of the bathroom. She rests her forehead on the plasticky beige surface of the door, annoyed but unsurprised to be kept waiting. Since Appa died, Suri's attention span has deteriorated. Now he will often start doing one thing and then stop halfway. In these moments he looks as though he is being pulled under, deep into a memory. One of Appa's lungis draped over the stair rail will turn Suri into a statue.

Sithara knocks again, harder. Still no response. She goes to her bedroom and returns with a five-cent coin, pushing it into the fake silver lock and turning until it pops open.

Suri is sitting on the closed lid of the toilet, resting his chin in his hands and staring at the wall. He doesn't flinch when she enters. His legs are longer than hers now, but his eyes behind large wire-rimmed spectacles are still gentle. She sits on the floor in front of him and leans her back against the wall.

What's wrong? she asks. She tries to sound casual. The silence between them stretches.

Ethan called me a cockroach, so I punched him, Suri says.

She frowns, unsure how to respond. Sithara's accent has faded; Suri's is still strong. She should be forcing him to talk to more people, to shake it. He stands and smooths his hair down in the mirror then shuts the door behind him, leaving Sithara sitting there. She sees a tiny pink razor on the bathroom sink, balled up tissues next to it. Suri was trying to shave.

She has been ripping out her own moustache with Amma's tweezers since before they even got here, after their cousin Nisal told her she had whiskers. That night she had stood in front of the bathroom mirror quivering, cursing the thick hairs that framed her upper lip, daring herself to pull. The first was so surprising; she could see the white root, slightly bulbous, and it made her feel clean. After a few she got the hang of it. She started to understand the tweezer's weight in her hands, that it was better to press the flat side against the skin than to dig the point in. The bloody mess left on the bench by Suri makes his task look more difficult. She clears the debris before brushing her teeth. She will have to tell Amma to buy him a real razor.

Mornings in the Fernando house are quiet now. Amma gets up before either of them and starts preparing food. Every morning she cooks something different – soaks pink lentils for parippu, roasts and grinds peanuts for gado gado or marinates chicken in cinnamon, chilli and cloves.

The three of them give each other a wide berth, each one vanishing when the other appears. The cold grey light of their kitchen in winter has started to feel normal. Back in

Colombo they lived in a bungalow where the doors stayed open even when it rained. Aunties and uncles came in and out, accusing one another of being too skinny. That house was never slack-jawed or gaping like this one, split open by Appa's absence.

Amma is frowning into the pantry. She is beautiful, although she doesn't seem to care. She has wide eyes and full rose lips, a nipped waist and tiny ankles. Men's eyes follow her with reverence and a touch of resignation, like she is someone else's Christmas present. Male grocery clerks hold her bags a little too close to their chest, so that Amma has to lean forward and brush their fingers with her own to retrieve her things. Sithara's principal at St Mary's, Mr Banks, always makes a beeline for Amma, leaving Sithara shuffling her feet. It is hard to be the daughter of a pretty widow.

The pantry smells faintly of dried coriander and star anise. In front of Amma are rows and rows of glass jars with white labels marked in scratchy cursive.

Green gram. Desiccated Coconut. Cornflakes. Wheat Flour. Besan.

She is probably trying to figure out if they have enough for dinner this week. To Sithara there is always an abundance of food, more than they can eat, but Amma never seems at ease. Without looking up from her list, she tells her to take some breakfast.

I'm not hungry, thank you, Amma, Sithara says.

She knows this will not sit well. But the thought of eating

idiyappam, drenched in the pale gold kiri hodi that sits on the stove, is too much to bear. Her nails will end up stained with turmeric and her classmates will notice.

Amma kisses her teeth, scolds her. I got up at five to cook for you, girl, she says.

Sithara and Suri walk their bikes down the pavement with the whole footpath between them. They have about a mile before the paths to their single-sex schools diverge. Invercargill is so flat that the sky itself seems bigger here.

They bike to school no matter the weather. On days like today they will arrive with chilblains on their fingers and toes. Sithara used to slam her hands on top of the bar heaters when she got to class, till she realised it only made them ache more.

She knows they look old-fashioned compared to their peers, that out of their school uniforms they both dress like it is still the seventies. But getting new clothes and hair wouldn't make them white.

Sometimes, after long days at school, Sithara feels like a cockroach too. Or a spider. Something low-bellied, scuttling across the toenails of a god. She feels her skin too thick on her muscles, her muscles too heavy for her bones. She feels her hair suddenly oily and notices it reeks of mustard seed. The other girls at her school don't even sweat. They have hair that swishes and flicks. Hers thuds against her back when she runs in PE. Every day she discovers a new way that she is ugly.

Tomorrow it will be a year, Suri says.

His voice has a strange note to it, as though something is trying to climb out. A year of Amma looking through them. A year of Suri coming home with bruises and cuts. A year of avoiding lavender soap and Appa's old records. A year of not-crying. They reach the crossroads and Suri cycles away without saying goodbye.

Sithara has two best friends – a Chinese girl called Libby Zhu and a white girl called Angela Pearson. Angela's head is shaped like a lightbulb. She lives over the road from Sithara with seven siblings and a dad who always gives Amma a hungry grin. He often comes over unannounced, checking if there's anything Amma 'needs a man' for. Amma keeps her replies short, civil. She wraps her arms around her body and shrinks as though her very dimensions might be an invitation. Sithara has never even seen her smile at any man other than Appa.

Libby's parents own the one takeaway restaurant in Invercargill that isn't fish and chips. It is popular, and she usually has to run home after school to help out. Sometimes Sithara comes along. Partly because Libby is hilarious and partly because it feels good to be around another family that is also at odds with this place.

Libby is quick-witted. She has a loud voice and long limbs and a totally different way of coping. Sithara retreats under pressure, tries to vanish, but Libby roars back. She is always on alert, takes pleasure in watching even her teachers squirm. She lasts for only twenty minutes in history, but being sent to Mr Banks' office for insolence doesn't seem to bother her.

Sithara files into the church between her friends. St Mary's is single-sex and Catholic, and each week they have mass with St Matthew's, Suri's school. When they pass their teacher, Mrs Brewer, she ignores them. A rumour went round school last year that Mrs Brewer's husband was seen kissing a man in Queens Park. This news rocked the entire student body for weeks – the girls were scandalised. Sithara found the thought of a whole community knowing something Mrs Brewer might not know terrifying.

Libby and Sithara are in Mrs Brewer's accelerated maths class and Libby watches her teacher's hands hungrily, waiting for her wedding ring to go missing, but the thin gold band is still cuffed to her finger. Her lips have grooves above them like someone has pulled a seam too tight. Libby says it's probably the stress of it all.

The air inside the church is colder than outside. Sithara tugs the sleeves of her school blazer over her hands. St Matthew's file in at the same time. The girls are all pretending not to notice, but there is a small charge of possibility in the air every time the two schools come together.

Angela starts to look anxious. Her long red hair smells

15

like fake pineapple. She has it pinned back on each side with plastic blue barrettes that are wildly un-regulation and she taps her fingers on the pews as she passes them. Sithara stops to tell her she looks pretty and sees Suri at the back of the church.

He's standing a little apart from the other boys. She rakes over the rest of them, trying to figure out which one might be Ethan, wanting to get the measure of him. She has the sudden urge to pick Suri up like a baby and carry him outside, to rub his back and sing 'You Send Me' the way Appa used to.

The priest, Father Lewis, has a raspy voice and thick white hairs sticking out of his nostrils. He starts the sermon in Latin, raising his arms while intoning. The consonants slip out without pause or variation. The steeple is so high the sound gets lost, so there is a microphone sticking out of the pulpit. The walls and ceiling are stained a light brown. The painted windows depict a Jesus who is sadder and skinnier than any Sithara saw in Sri Lanka.

Sithara closes her eyes and pictures herself home in Colombo, alone, standing in the middle of their small garden. A family of squirrels visited every morning. Birds would eat the papaw skins Appa threw out to them once she and Suri were finished. The air settles over her like a warm blanket. She can hear tuktuks and children playing. Her hair feels alive again. She imagines stealing a can of condensed milk and a knife from the kitchen, running into the garden, piercing the top and sucking it out.

Angela squeezes Sithara's arm and she realises with a jolt the priest is looking right at her. He is reading out the names of people who have died. Father Lewis is trying to say Appa's name.

Ravi, he says. Like it rhymes with 'savvy'. She turns again to check on Suri but cannot find him. Father Lewis says, Doctor Ravi Fernando's work at Southland Hospital was appreciated, especially by the most vulnerable members of our parish.

He doesn't mention how many of the parish's most vulnerable refused to let *The Indian* touch them. Sithara looks at the floor so she doesn't have to make eye contact with anyone, and tries to slow her breathing. In the reflection of the church's cold glassy tiles she re-imagines herself. As someone terribly powerful, someone who can doom people with a single glance, like a gorgon.

She grinds her teeth, chews them to dust, opens her mouth and lets ash fall out. In the grit she tastes the horrified looks of the priest and the schoolchildren and her sour-lipped teachers. She summons demons from her stomach and vomits lava over everyone stupid enough to look at her.

Sithara grabs the end of her plait and holds it, trying to calm down. Her hair doesn't grab back like it used to, but it is still coarse and strong. Libby is glowering at the priest. Angela is distracted, looking between the lectern and Fraser Duncan, who is standing one pew behind theirs on the opposite side. He's lanky, with thick blond hair. Sithara can sort of see why he makes the girls swoon. He looks like he belongs in a milk ad.

At lunchtime, Sithara, Angela and Libby sit at low wooden tables behind the music block, sharing the cigarettes Angela steals from her dad. They take turns clamping them between their middle and index fingers and propping them on the edge of their lips, practising looking practised. They huddle close to ward off the cold.

Angela draws elaborate scenes on her thighs under her skirt in blue biro. Today she is drawing the back of Fraser Duncan's head, staring at her knickers with his arms outstretched.

His tongue must be enormous if he can reach from there, says Sithara.

It's fucking *huge*, says Angela.

Libby enthusiastically ashes her cigarette and drops the whole thing onto her skirt. She hops, shrieking while Angela slaps her legs to put it out.

The next day Sithara gets up an hour earlier than usual. She doesn't want to see her grief reflected in Suri. He must have had the same thought, because she heard nothing from his room, or the bathroom, before she left.

Six in the morning in winter is dark and empty but

Sithara finds peace in solitude. She cycles with her head down, carefully, sticking to the middle of the road to avoid the black ice. This is also how she avoids peeking into houses where families might be waking up and getting ready for school and work, together.

The night of Appa's funeral, she was unable to get into the bathroom. It was the first time she tried the coin. She waited outside, stood, then sat. She pressed her ear to the door and called but got no reply. The house was quiet, so after fifteen minutes she figured the lock must have stuck. She cast around for something thin and hard. She tried a bobby pin from her hair first but snapped it in the process. Then she shoved a coin into the lock and it turned easily. It was like it had been waiting for her to figure it out.

She was hot from the victory. Her neck was on fire and the ends of her fingers were tingling like she could shoot sparks out of them if she concentrated hard enough. Like if she had held onto the side of her appa's coffin for one minute longer she might have been able to shock him back to life. She slammed the door open, flushed, to find Amma in the middle of a sea of her own hair. There were huge lengths coiled up and little piles of curls on top, like a carpet of dark roses. Amma's tiny feet looked out of place in the middle, shocking, as she glared at herself in the mirror and snipped the rest away. Her face was so small without it.

Sithara was sickened by the sight of Amma's naked head. She was speechless, betrayed. Amma didn't even acknowledge the intrusion. She looked like a person who had been slashed open. She rubbed her fingers over the back and then cut the hairs at the nape of her neck closer to the skin.

The street is lit by a persistent moon. Sithara rounds an icy corner and a small figure appears in front of her. It is Suri. There is light enough for Sithara to see he doesn't have his bike and is facing away. She calls his name, and as he turns she sees there is blood dripping from his chin.

Scared and unsure, she slows down her pedalling. Suri looks away, then again at her, waving his hand. He is shooing her back the way she came. Dread rises in her throat. Suri urges her away again, but Sithara keeps pedalling. She speeds up. She calls, Annah! I am coming.

And then she sees why Suri was warning her. There is a black car parked horizontally, several metres away, its engine idling. The road has a very slight rise in the middle, like they are parked on a piece of swollen earth. The exhaust is sputtering dirty smoke. Three boys are inside.

They look older. They all have roughly the same shade of brown hair and freckles. The two in the front are relaxed, drinking from a bottle in a paper bag, passing a cigarette or a joint back and forth. Smoke drifts out the open window. The boy in the back is in his school uniform, quiet. He stares at Sithara with eyes glinting, his lips pressed together tight.

In front of their car is Suri's bike. It has been deformed

by the car's tyres. Warped like it was always some flimsy, impermanent thing. Appa gave them the bikes for Christmas. Suri and Sithara walked into the living room and saw one blue, one red, parked side by side, each with silver bows on the handlebars. Suri grabbed Appa round the waist and thanked him over and over again. Appa told Suri he was mistaken, that the bikes were for him and Amma, he just wanted the children to admire them. Sithara can still remember the sound of Amma laughing in the kitchen.

She dismounts by Suri and they stand shoulder to shoulder.

The fellow in the back is Ethan, Suri says, keeping his eyes on the car. Those are his brothers. They're drunk. His voice cracks.

So this is Cockroach Boy, Sithara says to Suri. Ethan leans out of the car window to take Sithara in and laughs.

There is no one to bear witness; the few houses on the street all look either empty or asleep. Ethan mouths 'faggot', spits it out like the word itself is dirty. It's a slur Sithara had never heard till they came to this country. She looks at Suri, his hands trembling. Appa's death, the move, her betrayal at Sigiriya, have torn pieces off of him. All she can see is how much he has shrunk.

Sithara turns her bike around and whispers to Suri.

Hop on when I do and don't look back, she says.

Is she going to help you, you reckon? Ethan says. He gets out of the car.

Physically he is not intimidating; he is ratty and lean with sloping shoulders. Despite this, he moves towards Sithara as though he could belt her and send her flying. She thinks about what Libby would do. She throws her plait over her shoulder, now.

Sithara springs onto her bike, and Suri sits in front of her on the frame, his hands gripping the bars right inside hers.

Ethan's laughter screeches, Where the fuck are you going?

Sithara places shaky feet on the pedals. They remember how to do this. They learned on Maude Aunty's rusty old bike in Colombo. She pushes off, heading for the corner.

The extra weight almost topples them, and Suri has to trail his toes lightly on the pavement for balance. He keeps his eyes on the road, wary of the shimmering ice. Sithara forces her legs to push the pedals down, her thighs burning. Behind them she can hear the car doors closing, the engine being turned on and stalling. It is much harder now than it was when Suri was five. If they die on this soulless street, Amma will be all alone.

Slowly Sithara picks up speed, her knees churning round. Suri leans his face into the wind, urging them forward. Sithara hits her stride, and Suri releases the ground. He's too long to tuck his legs like he used to, and he winces when the frame judders beneath him, but his hands under hers clasp on tight, copy her tilt, follow as she guides the bike.

In the strong wind, strands of hair unravel from her plait to flap alongside her. She feels a rush of adrenaline and wonders if Suri feels it too. They have almost made it to the corner when the car gets going.

Sithara can feel it pulling closer. If it hits them, their bodies will be destroyed like Suri's bike.

Come on, Thara, Suri says, low under his breath.

Just before she rounds the corner she slows her pedalling, letting the momentum of the bike carry them through the sharp turn. Then she whispers a prayer to Appa.

They lurch deeply into the turn and Suri gasps. She sees the black ice to their left. A wide strip running like a lethal river close to the side of the road. She straightens her elbows, trying to pull both of them upright.

There was a before and there is an after. Where she and Suri are now is in the after, and they can never go back. In the seconds where they are almost horizontal, skidding round the bend with a drunk driver barrelling towards them, she pictures death a thousand times. Death in this town where no one likes them, where their funerals will be an embarrassment, where the priest will stumble over their names before he puts them in the ground, more death for the house that already knows it so well, more grief for Amma who doesn't seem to remember any other feeling.

The car bites at their heels and there is a scream as it hits ice. People must be leaping out of their beds, ripping curtains in their haste. Far away from them, Sithara can hear a front door opening, a sharp cry.

She looks over her shoulder. The car coasts behind them

at an unnatural angle. Its wheels are useless and the boys inside have their mouths wide open.

When the car swallows a wooden telephone pole, the crash is loud like a song – windows popping, doors caving, metal meeting bone. The silence after the crash is unbearable. Sithara and Suri clear the corner but Sithara keeps pedalling, gasping for air now. It can't hit her lungs fast enough.

Her hair has completely burst out of its plait. It feels so good to have her hair back to normal that Sithara has to laugh. Suri is close to her and he is safe. She squeezes his hands.

Sithara feels the slight sting of tears forming in her eyes, and then, relief. She thought she had forgotten how to cry.

Josephina
1951, Singapore

Josephina Colette Paluvettaraiyar sets her family's breakfast on the table and looks down the length of the dining room. Down the hallway, in the good room, a solid marble statue of the Virgin Mary looks back, open palms offering benediction.

Josephina dusts her hands on her kurta, shivering her bracelets and disrupting the silence with thin clinks. The drapes have been pulled. She can smell the tang of wood polish. Visitors are coming today.

Although Josephina is just ten years old, her father's only wish, and main occupation, is finding Josephina a husband. Each time potential suitors come to their house, Josephina ties her hair in a bun, pushes her feet into silk slippers and stands as still as she can while her mother wraps her sari. Then, when her mother leaves to greet the guests, Josephina sits in her room and pulls at her face in the mirror. She tugs her cheeks, squashes her nose, twists her lips into a snarl, prods every tooth with the tip of her tongue until her face feels like something that belongs to her again. Or until her mother raps on the bedroom door and beckons Josephina out.

Breakfast for her father is eggs with onion and green chilli. He prefers them more like an omelette than scrambled – thin strips of chilli and onion nestled under folds of golden egg. Josephina has hacked the chilli into fat cubes and almost coddled the egg. It rests on his plate in a congealed mound. Cheese toast for her mother, who likes the cheese crispy, served piping hot, still bubbling in the middle. Josephina barely turned the oven on. The cheese melted ever so slightly then cooled and hardened.

Breakfast for her Pātti is runny oats flavoured with just a little salt, cooked in water. Josephina has made Pātti's porridge exactly as she likes it – the consistency of congee, lukewarm, in a wide bowl half-full so Pātti can hold her head over it and avoid spilling. Josephina will eat oats too. Not because she enjoys them, she just likes to be the same as Pātti.

Josephina's father enters and takes his seat without looking at her. He has the same distinct cheekbones as Josephina. He's clever, too clever to waste love on his family. He sees Josephina as currency, her mother as the maid and Pātti as an inconvenience.

Recently her father has been coming home late. He

wakes the whole house when he staggers inside. He starts arguments with her mother about money, loud enough for everyone to hear. This morning he frowns at his eggs but eats them anyway, flipping through the newspaper.

Pātti hobbles in, Josephina's mother steadying her. She stops in the doorway, shakes off the assistance and holds out her arms. She makes a low, happy growl when Josephina steps into her embrace.

Pātti was born in Pondicherry. She speaks Tamil, French, English and Malay. Her skin is soft as rose petals and her nose is pierced on both sides with large gold discs. She's dark-skinned, a real Tamil girl, with a widow's peak she sharpens with a razor. The fat rubies she wears to church drag her earlobes to her shoulders.

Once a week Josephina sits on the floor of their bathroom while Pātti lathers her whole body in black soap and tells stories about her home. About climbing trees, killing snakes and tricking her way into French mansions — just so she could look around and feel what it was like to be special. She rubs her fingers hard into Josephina's scalp while she works in the shampoo and it feels like she is massaging every fear Josephina has ever had away.

Pātti's good humour and cleverness helped her snag a Eurasian for a husband. She was married at sixteen, widowed at thirty, and left with a light-skinned daughter.

Money ran out fast. Pātti started an informal day care, and though still a child herself, Josephina's mother was made to cook and clean. Children too young to go to school would be dropped off by their parents in the morning and collected late at night.

Josephina doesn't understand why her mother and Pātti do not get on. It has always been this way. When she was very young she had hoped to change it. She can remember sitting on Pātti's lap with her mother close, trying to fold their hands together.

It may be that when her husband died, Pātti leaned a little too much on her child for support. Or perhaps Josephina's mother envied the affection Pātti bestowed on children whose parents could pay for it. Josephina can't imagine her dear Pātti ever being unkind, but occasionally she observes them both and wonders what she doesn't know.

Josephina's mother takes one look at the cold toast and hard cheese and pushes the plate away. She has pleasant but forgettable features. A double chin. Bright eyes behind spectacles that don't suit her face. She works as a nurse.

Sometimes she calls Josephina 'Azab', which means 'doom' in Malay.

Josephina was born in the good room, under Mother Mary's gaze, on 8 December 1941. The first day bombs fell like rain over Singapore. Pātti spread towels on the kitchen floor and delivered the baby herself. Her daughter was in labour for seventy-two hours.

Pātti recalls the story of Josephina's birth as though it is an epic. She says they were woken first by the screams of air-raid sirens. They gathered in the good room, terrified, and the pigs in the swamp outside squealed like they were competing. Josephina's father took shelter under his bed and didn't come out until the ack-ack guns stopped roaring.

The house was filled with cold fear and agony. The walls curved, skirting death, and when Josephina emerged, her cry shattered the windows. And despite Pātti enjoying the story, savouring the tale of her granddaughter being born against all odds while the Japanese brought the city to its knees, Josephina feels as though her destiny was written in blood.

During the occupation, when Josephina was still a toddler, her mother would sneak out, leaving her with Pātti, to help families in the area surrounding their house. When it was over, she started working at Kandang Kerbau hospital. She came home exhausted, with a short temper.

Josephina has always known her mother doesn't like her. She gets a look on her face when she sees Josephina, like there is a bad smell. She doesn't hold her, or even touch her if not to prepare her for an audience. Josephina suspects that her and Pātti's closeness reopens a wound. Or perhaps her mother was unable to grow attached to a child who brought the kamikazes with her, who was born amid so much death. But Pātti loves her enough for the both of them.

Have your makan early and be dressed for visitors by two o'clock, her father says as he leaves. Pātti's lip curls and her eyes follow him out the door.

Don't dress too nicely, Josie, she says, slurping her porridge.

Pātti must have seen something different in her father's behaviour today. Josephina nods.

Her mother is silent. Usually she tells Josephina what sari to wear, that she must clean her slippers, fix her hair like so. But today she just shrugs and waves her away.

Potential suitors have been visiting since Josephina was seven. She is practiced now at receiving them, at serving ginger ale and sponge cake with jam and cream.

Now that she's older, whole families will come. The mothers ask the most questions. They are curious about her skills in the kitchen, and they seem equally delighted and enraged by Josephina's looks. They grab her chin and turn it from side to side. They sieve her, trying to shake out a flaw. They release her with disdain when they fail to.

Josephina has light eyes that are the exact same colour as a pile of gold. She has full lips that curve upwards and eyebrows that are a world unto their own. They have a wispy base that starts just where her lashes end, thick hairs in the body, and in the middle they grow straight and then lean towards their sister — almost becoming one. Framing a face that makes strangers sigh.

The sons that come range from younger than Josephina by a couple of years to older than her by ten. The young ones are uncomfortable in their shirts and stiff shoes. They stare longingly at the fields out the window. The teenage ones sit in smug conspiracy with their fathers, looking at her face like they created it themselves. None of the sons ask Josephina any questions.

Josephina despises them all. Her cheeks burn. She sits mute, staring at the floor, distracts herself by fetching tea or cleaning cake crumbs off Pātti's collar. She spends the hour or less that the meetings take feeling ill. None of the girls in her year at school have to sit through these things so young. Many of them will likely be married in the same way, but most parents wait until their daughters are older, at least sixteen.

Very occasionally, the visitors have no apparent sons at all. These men are the ones with real money. On these days, her father trims his moustache with purpose and slicks his hair with Brylcreem. He opens the door smoothly and whisks them into the kitchen for Scotch and cigarettes.

One of these times, foolishly, Josephina answered the door alone. The man on the other side was Chinese. Older than her father. As wide as the doorway itself. Solid gold rings on his fingers. He bowed to Josephina and smiled like a wolf. Her father hurried to the door to greet him and the two of them went straight to the kitchen. The sponge cake had sagged by the time the big man left in a huff. Josephina still doesn't know why he was turned away.

A month ago, she was led by one of the nuns at school to the high fence surrounding the grounds. Most of the nuns who teach at the school are bullies. There's only one Josephina cares for. Her name is Sister Kirby and she teaches English. She has spectacles so large that all her expressions seem magnified. Her accent sounds like music. She gave Josephina a copy of *Jane Eyre* six months ago and said she could keep it as long as she liked.

Sister Murphy knocked on the classroom door during elocution and beckoned to Josephina. The girls in her class giggled. She packed her books and followed dumbly. At the fence, Sister Murphy greeted the Malay gentleman beside Josephina's father with a nod. He wore dark sunglasses and had a wide forehead that reflected the sun. He asked Josephina to bare her teeth, like a horse.

Then he pulled a delicate handkerchief from his pocket, wiped his forehead and said, I'm not taking a wife who needs her teeth out in ten years, Uncle.

Josephina bikes through the field to her friend Mavis's house. The sun is high and she has hours to do as she pleases. Their house in Changi is close to a rubber plantation and is surrounded on one side by a swamp. There is a little grey cat that visits occasionally. A kitten, with a silky belly. Josephina is trying to tame her. She allows herself to be stroked but refuses to come inside.

There are farmers of all kinds in the fields. The Chinese grow flowers and vegetables, keep ducks and turkeys. The Indians have little goats and herds of buffalo and cows that chew on the hibiscus hedges as they pass.

Freedom like this is rare for Josephina. She is barefoot, excited to push the afternoon out as far as she can without earning a whack from her mother on return. Though sometimes the beating is worth it.

Mavis is Chinese. She lives with her parents, both sets of grandparents and four younger siblings in a small house with a rusted zinc roof. Mavis opens the door and shouts with happiness when Josephina holds up bamboo rods. She has a short, boyish haircut and dimples on both cheeks when she smiles.

Walking into Mavis's house feels the same as walking into a hug from Pātti. The kitchen is filled with warm steam from the bones boiling into stock on the stove. Every room is overflowing and comfortable. There are buckets of clean washing on chairs, children's toys sprinkled on the ground through the hallway. Mavis's two older siblings are in the sitting room with kittens on their laps, their mother gently cleaning the kittens' eyes with a rag.

They head straight to Mavis's kitchen, dodging her four-year-old brother's fists, to melt rubber bands in hot oil and dip the ends of the rods in the paste before anyone scolds them for being wasteful. Then they ride their bikes to the pond and stand at the water's edge, holding the rods sticky side up.

The pond is green and squidgy, scarcely deeper than their ankles. It smells like pig shit. Every time the rain comes it floods and spills out into the surrounding fields. Josephina works her feet into the mud. A bright blue dragonfly darts onto the end of Mavis's rod and sticks.

His wings are translucent, the tiny corners edged in sapphire. His body is so radiant it looks out of place above the shit-filled pond. Mavis pulls the creature down and holds him right in front of her eyes. She laughs mercilessly, twirling him around, and his wings vibrate as if he is still free.

✦

When Josephina returns half an hour late, Pātti is already sitting in the good room in anticipation, stationed in her wooden chair. Pātti turns her nose up at English couches, swearing they will ruin her posture. Good girl, she says when she sees Josephina covered in mud.

Pātti lies in wait only when the visitor is a single man. She is not as intimidating as she believes she is, but her silent judgement of every suitor who enters is usually reassuring. Less so today.

Pātti flicks her index finger under Josephina's jaw and pulls her close. Her black eyes are filmy, ringed with blue. Pātti got old with no warning.

This one is rich, she says. Be careful. I fear your father has made up his mind.

Josephina feels her stomach roll, instinct urging her to run.

Pātti's voice is hoarse and she seems drowsy. She nods as though her warning has been sufficient and smiles without joy. Her teeth and gums are stained from the betel. She sucks a huge wash of saliva back into her mouth and spits bright red juice into her tin with a hollow splash. There are three quick knocks on the door.

Azab, he is here, Josephina's mother calls from the other room.

An Englishman. He wears a cream linen suit. When he takes off his jacket, the hairs covering his forearms are reddish, thick and fuzzy like fur. He introduces himself as Mr Brooks and his accent catches the air, making Pātti frown.

Josephina's mother and father walk in behind him. They stop, aghast at her muddy ankles and knotted hair. She still has pond scum beneath her fingernails.

Alamak! I thought I told you to be ready for two, her father says under his breath like a hiss.

Mr Brooks is old, maybe fifty. Josephina and her mother arrange themselves on the couch in front of the window. It has been pushed back to allow room for all of them to fit. Josephina's head is right under Mother Mary's bare feet. Her father and Mr Brooks sit on the couch facing opposite. Mr Brooks is a head taller than her father. He has meaty lips and a ginger moustache.

Josephina should have listened to her stomach and stayed away, she could have hid at Mavis's house. Being dragged home and belted for her insolence would have been better still than this, than staring at this wrinkled face and imagining it looming over her at night-time. How many years will she have to suffer his touch?

Pātti starts snoring in her chair. Josephina smirks, at least she has her teammate. She can always rely on Pātti to help sabotage the carefully laid plans of her parents.

To be clear, I am here for my son, Mr Brooks says.

Oh! Josephina says, startling her mother. Mr Brooks continues talking as though he has not heard her. He looks just above Josephina's head, giving her the disconcerting feeling that he is speaking to someone else.

Alfred is a fine lad, he continues. When he has completed his studies at Oxford, you will make him a good wife. He pauses and his eyes dart around Josephina like he is following a mosquito. His mother was quite the rose herself. She died during the invasion, God rest her soul.

Saliva flies from his mouth and lands on his lap.

Mr Brooks has houses in Singapore, England and India, her father says, Alfred is an excellent match for you.

Her father continues asking Mr Brooks about his son. Outside, on the street, the rojak man announces his wares with a hoarse cry. Josephina can hear children playing. She wishes she was still with Mavis, fighting over who caught the prettiest dragonfly. Pātti's grand old head is tucked like a bird hiding her face in her wings. Her mother still hasn't said a word.

Alfie doesn't know that I am here, Mr Brooks says, his eyes still shifting round the room. But I trust he will be pleased with my decision.

Her father and Mr Brooks stand up to shake hands. They move to the kitchen.

Josephina is surprised to feel her stomach easing up, rumbling for some sponge cake, and cuts herself a slice. She is not averse to being a well-kept woman in England. A man showing up with intentions only for his son is nothing to be afraid of. Yes, she will be married to someone she has not met. But not for years. She will be allowed to finish her schooling. She pictures herself in a car, being driven around the streets of London wearing gloves, a frothy hat perched on the side of her head. Josephina takes a big bite of her cake. She hears the scrape of the Scotch bottle being pulled from the top of the cupboard.

Thank you, Ammi, Josephina says. She almost never calls her mother this. If her mother notices, she ignores it. She seems nervous, and she stands abruptly to haul an almost limp Pātti up. Josephina wipes her lips and rises to help, but her mother shakes her head no and takes Pātti to the door.

Where are you going? Josephina asks.

Stay here, Azab, it won't take long. Her mother avoids her eyes.

Glasses clink in the kitchen. Josephina lies on the couch alone. What won't take long? Her mother is always cold, often direct, and she hates secrets. Even if the news is delivered curtly, she tells Josephina what is going on.

Laying down, Josephina finishes her cake, balancing the plate on her flat chest and picking it apart bit by bit, crumbling the last pieces into her mouth and enjoying the sun beaming through the window onto her face.

She wonders if she is being used as a kind of a surprise. Mr Brooks not telling his son that he is looking for his wife is so strange. But even though the father is unnerving, the son could be different. Josephina has never seen much of herself reflected in her own parents.

Maybe she will ask Mr Brooks to show her a photo of Alfred. Alfie. When Pātti returns she will tell her that she is happy, that in spite of the torture of endless families looking down their noses at Josephina even as they try to claim her, things have worked out just fine.

The door opens like an intake of breath and ushers in Mr Brooks. Josephina jolts and her plate slides to the floor, rattling to a stop. He smiles, making eye contact with her for the first time.

Hello, dear.

The door closes without Mr Brooks touching the handle. Her father's hand, sealing them inside. Mr Brooks lays his jacket across the arm of the couch. His palm slithers across his lapel, smoothing it flat.

She can hear her heart thump in her ears, a moth throwing itself at a lightbulb. A small whimper escapes Josephina, betraying her. She counts the steps it will take to get to the door, trying to calculate whether Mr Brooks is big enough to block it without shifting his weight. He is still looking right at her. Unsmiling, as though he is trying to calculate something too.

Mr Brooks unbuckles his belt. Josephina feels the air seize around her. If only she had rubbed pig shit into her hair. If only she had stayed out with Mavis all day. If only she had left the good room as soon as it was empty. If only Pātti was here.

She runs for the door but he throws the belt like a whip, lashing her. Josephina's knees crash to the ground and she cries out in pain. He wraps the belt around her neck and hauls her, face down, onto the couch. Josephina claws at the air. She wonders if she will die. He easily climbs on top of her.

It is no vindication to realise that her worst fears are actually her reality, that they will happen in the same room in which she was born. It is remarkable how quickly a room becomes a cage.

Josephina's perception of herself as a child vanishes. Even though a stranger could tell she is largely unloved, she has clung to something. Whether it was a trick of biology or even just duty, she thought her parents cared for her a little.

If only she had run faster.

His weight is like the ceiling crushing her. She tries to yell for Pātti. The couch is solid as a funeral pyre, covered in crumbs. She is not sure what is happening but it feels like she is being mauled. He pulls away from her for a second to struggle with her skirt. She bellows once more for her Pātti and then all she feels is pain. It consumes her. It is like drowning in the dark. Like black liquid pouring into her eyes and ears and throat.

She leaves her body entirely and watches from above. This is how she realises she is still making noise. She is spluttering like a bird being strangled, but Mr Brooks doesn't stop.

A tuneless buzzing fills Josephina's ears, loud and unbreaking, replacing the sound of her own cries. It feels like the heralding of some unholy knowledge that has been coiled inside her, waiting. She was always for sale. Mr Brooks was just the first man who could afford her.

And then there is something else. Something more important, that washes her mind clean and sends her back to her body just as he rolls off of her, panting.

Josephina moves fast. She rips the belt away from her neck and climbs onto the arm of the couch. She reaches for the windowsill, pulling herself up, the air clearing the further she gets from him. She slots her two small feet in, braces her back against the window frame and takes Mother Mary by the shoulder, the marble smooth and cold against her fingers.

Josephina pulls at the statue once, heaving her forward, twice, and her feet teeter at the edge. One last shove takes all the strength she has left, but Mother Mary gives, tips forward and sails past Josephina towards the couch, sinking into the old man's head like a foot in mud. Her screams may not have brought her father into the room, but the crack of stone on a man's skull does. He rushes in to see Josephina backlit, squatting on the windowsill.

Her father stares at the Englishman lying dead in the good room and the colour drains from his face. He gives Josephina a look of horror, but whatever is on her face in response cows him.

Courage leaks out of her body, but Josephina has no fear to replace it, no shame. Mr Brooks, legs draped over the arm of the couch, blood staining the rug, isn't as tall as she had thought.

Go to your room, her father says. Don't come out until I call you.

She walks slowly to her bedroom and stands by the bed, breathing in and out, listening. Her back is throbbing from where the belt buckle hit her. Her neck stings. She can feel deep grooves from the edges of the belt around her throat like a collar. She can't bear to sit and feel that pain too. That scratching emptiness. Like a message has been hacked into her, telling her she is not a person, she is just a girl.

Someone is dead but it's not her. She is damned forever but she is still alive. She hears thumps, moving furniture, something dull and heavy slipping down the stairs.

It is the last time Josephina ever sees her father.

Annie
2018, London

Annie refuses Suri's help and hauls her suitcase up the stairs to his spare bedroom. Houses back home don't have stairways this narrow. She walks backwards, pulling it up with awkwardly outstretched arms, and the corner of it catches Suri's pristine white walls.

Fuck, she says.

Are you okay? Suri calls.

She tries to clean the mark with the sleeve of her shirt but it doesn't budge, remaining as evidence of Annie being somewhere she shouldn't.

I left a mark. On your wall. I'm so sorry.

Suri waves her apology away without looking up.

Oh, okay, she says. He hasn't even asked why she's here yet. She was so ready to defend herself that it feels like an anticlimax.

Suri makes the bed just like Gran. No top sheet. He

avoids touching the space where Annie's head will go. He even flicks the pillow covers to snap out the wrinkles. The white slips are empty like sleep with no dreams.

His house is intimidating, deliberate. The light fixtures have complicated steel shades around them. The walls have well-framed photos of city streets and attractive smiling people. The windows are so long. His rooms are bathed in light.

Suri finishes making the bed and stands up straight, looking at Annie across it, hands on his hips. We use this as a study mostly, he says, but it's warm enough.

She is too tired to ask who 'we' is.

He leaves a towel on the desk and says he'll be downstairs if she needs anything. She wants to express her gratitude. To tell him how unexpected and comforting it is to be welcomed in without question. But no word she has to say thank you is big enough.

Annie showers and finds a t-shirt to wear to bed in a daze. She's about to lie down when she notices the photo on the bedside table. She has looked at this photo so many times she knows it by heart. Her mum's copy is in a thin metal frame, leaves patterned along the top and bottom. Annie could close her eyes and recall every curve of those leaves, feel the soft fuzzy material on the back. In Hamilton it sat by the TV, in Christchurch it was next to her mum's bed.

This copy is in a glass frame, just two panels with the photo inside, so that it looks like it is floating. Annie can see the very edges of the photo for the first time. The pavement has weeds growing up out of its cracks. There are three people standing above it, on the doorstep of a red house. A man with hair like a young Moose Ali Khan. He looks just past the camera to the person taking the photo, like he is trying to invite her in. A chubby boy wearing glasses peers up at him, his hand covering his mouth like he is trying not to laugh at something the man said.

And a solemn girl. Her dark, pretty skin gleams. Her hair is so large it could swallow her. It's Annie's mum, Suri, and their dad Ravi. Annie picks it up; she has always adored the way her grandfather looks at the photographer, at Gran. Like all he wants is to have her closer. Annie came here alone, but she didn't come just for herself.

She lies down. Her stomach aches with all the questions she has for Suri. On the plane she tried making a list, but looking at them made her feel pathetic.

Do you miss Gran?

How much do you know about me?

Do you love us?

Why did you leave?

Why didn't you come back?

Annie wakes up muddled and pokes around for her phone. It's just before midnight. She slept for sixteen hours. Her surroundings shift and settle into place. The curtains are open; she must have forgotten to pull them. There is so much noise floating up from the road.

She checks her messages. There is one from her mum she deletes without reading, her finger like a wave wiping the shoreline clean. She texts Gran and her best friend Monica to let them know she's arrived safely. She avoids specifying where.

A bookcase is built into the wall opposite and she crawls closer to try to get a read on her uncle. There's a collection of John Pilger essays, old copies of the *New Yorker* with their pages stuck together, and everything else is recipe books: Madhur Jaffrey, Claudia Roden, a fat tome by Marcella Hazan. She imagines Suri and a well-dressed, age-appropriate girlfriend flicking through recipe books together.

The house is quiet. Annie is wide awake. She should have listened to Monica's advice about pushing through her jet lag and staying up. But at least it gives her the chance to take in the house on her own, see how her uncle lives, see what sort of life she shoved her way into.

Rubber house shoes are waiting at the end of her bed. They're a little big but they work for creeping. 'Creeping' makes Annie giggle. This gives her a sharp pang of missing Nia desperately. She forces it down.

When Annie finds the kitchen, Suri is sitting at the breakfast bar, disrupting her investigation. He's wearing a black bathrobe with gold cuffs and staring into a cup of tea. His bald head is even shinier under the kitchen light. He nods at Annie and asks if she would like some.

She says yes, apologetically, feeling caught out, feeling too scruffy to be in his house.

Were you waiting for me? Annie asks.

No. Sleeping just isn't a talent of mine, Suri says.

Annie can't relate and so she gives an odd hum in response, which she immediately regrets. She hunts for something else to talk about.

Your robe's Versace.

It was my Christmas present, Suri says.

He takes it off, revealing humble flannel pyjamas, and hangs it on Annie. It envelops her and pools around her feet. Annie finds her reflection in a round mirror above the microwave.

Take it back, it makes me feel poor, she says.

Suri laughs and Annie giggles a little back, surprising herself. His laugh is the best kind, contagious.

You must be hungry. There's a Turkish place up the road that's open all night?

I could eat, she says. She pulls out the stool next to him.

Me and Mum had a breakfast bar like this in Hamilton, she tells him, taking a breath and running her fingers over the wood, which is light and smooth. Actually, no, it wasn't this nice.

There are cups drying on a dish rack, a rotating wheel of

spices, and something that Annie recognises as the kind of pan Gran uses for hoppers. There are less familiar things too: a Nespresso machine, a whiteboard stuck to the fridge with two schedules on it, a drinks cart with bottles of whiskey and crystal tumblers.

Annie has spent her adult years living lightly. She's moved through shared flats and hotel rooms, uncertain when the next gig is coming, scared to settle down. Little real security. This is the household of people who have enough money to enjoy their life, and do. She can feel it, all the happy times. She didn't know how much she wanted something like this until now.

I'm a stunty, she says, hoping he will be amazed.

A stunt double?

TV shows, mostly. Films when I'm lucky. They pay better.

Is it dangerous? Suri asks.

Annie thinks about the directors who sign off on fire stunts without checking with health and safety, about the number of times she's been asked to cut short her rehearsal so they can get the first take. She wants to impress Suri so she shrugs.

Only when I'm off my game.

Suri gets up and makes her tea. He passes his phone over so Annie can order what she wants from the restaurant. He has a much bigger iPhone than her. And a brown leather case with a flap like all the over-forties.

Annie is used to people being at least intrigued when she

tells them about her profession. But she can't tell if Suri is shocked or just underwhelmed. Annie doubles for any actress under five foot five. Most of them are white. On set they put her in blonde wigs and tell her to keep out of the sun.

Suri clears his throat, How's your mother? he asks.

Mum? I don't know, she says, leaving the room emptier.

He hesitates, cherrypicks his next words. You don't talk to her?

Not much, since she got back with my dad.

Sithara

1986, Dunedin

Sithara wonders whether she should turn around and go home. Three afternoons a week she is a receptionist in a dentist's practice. Today there is scaffolding choking the building. Sheets of opaque plastic blind the windows. Tins of paint are stacked in columns at the entrance as though guarding it. Sithara stands before it all, blinking. Her hair ripples, tugging her away.

Moving to Dunedin for University has changed Sithara. She is louder now, a little more hungry. Sometimes she even speaks before she is invited to. Already she has plans to study abroad for a year of her degree – England or Scotland, maybe. Her choices are limited by the English she has been confined to for almost a decade now.

She doesn't think there are many Sri Lankans living in Scotland, but nothing could be worse than being Sri Lankan in New Zealand. Sithara is nursing a fluttering hope, bright and persistent, of being at the edge of a life she can't yet picture.

The first time Sithara walked into LAWS 101 the hairs on her arms stood up. A moment of panic in the doorway as she struggled to find somewhere to sit. There were a few whispers, dirty looks from the girls. Someone she didn't know waved, a man laughed in the corner of the lecture theatre, up by the windows.

Sithara has become hardened to her own visibility. She chose to believe she wasn't the joke and walked to a spare seat in the front. Her hair mercifully drew in front of her face like curtains. It was a couple of days before anyone sat next to her.

At first she was intimidated by the work, but her perspective shifted when she realised there was nothing to stop her being good at it. There was no one like her doing this, and so no one to say how it should be done. Sithara wasn't interested in making friends at University, she has Libby and Angela. She flats with a nice enough couple, Linda and Steve, who have got her into running. She calls Suri every other night. Amma sends her packages of food.

Every morning before sunrise she runs out of the city into the hills, accompanied only by her steady breath and the sound of her feet beating the pavement into submission, putting lengths of artless space behind her. Just before she turns back she stands for a moment at the top of Signal Hill, staring at the isolated village-town she has started to feel at home in.

On Friday evenings Libby and Angela come over for dinner. Usually they end up eating toast, drinking wine and going out. But sometimes they try out their burgeoning cooking skills on each other. Libby has decided she needs to master the art of a cheese souffle before she turns twenty-one.

Since moving out, Sithara has been lightly experimenting with her look. Today she is wearing earrings – plastic purple triangles that dangle bright against her skin – and a new hairstyle, two ponytails on top of her head, the strands twisted together and pinned to create a large, messy bun. Amma would surely curl her lip and attack it with a hairbrush. But the sun is shining bright and today, leaving her flat, Sithara almost felt pretty.

The window above her creaks open. A pale muscled arm reaches out, followed by a face. The face grins down at her.

Can I help you? he asks.

Sithara gestures to the entranceway. I work here, she says. I can't get in.

The window closes and the man himself reappears in the doorway. He leans his back against the doorframe so Sithara can pass by, but she hesitates. He is staring at her, smiling like the two of them already know one another.

He has light green eyes and smooth glossy cheeks. The bridge of his nose is peeling from sunburn. He's much taller than Sithara, with joyful lines decorating his mouth and eyes. He smells like clean bedsheets. She can feel her cheeks getting hot as she brushes past and walks upstairs to reception.

—

A week later, at Dunedin's only cinema, she sees him in the foyer. It is a brutally cold evening and the place is full.

He is standing in a group of men. He wears Levi's and work boots covered in splotches of white paint. One of his friends appears drunk, talks too loudly, grabs him by the neck and laughs when he is pushed off. Sithara stares at his shoulders. She imagines his hard hairless body under his shirt, his chest pressing down on hers.

Sithara thought she was looking discreetly but Angela follows her gaze and laughs.

Paul Fischer? she asks.

Sithara shakes her head and walks quickly towards the theatre.

No, I'm into it. He's hot. Angela takes her arm.

I don't know. Libby looks back over her shoulder. His ex-girlfriend is in my sociology class and the way he ditched her was kind of brutal.

He's single? Sithara asks, the pitch of her voice surprising them all.

Libby and Angela grin at each other over her head before the darkness of the cinema engulfs them.

Sylvester Stallone strides into a bar and Paul finds Sithara, leans in, mouth very close to her cheek, and tells her there is an empty seat beside him. He draws her to it and offers the straw of his Coke. A strand of her hair grazes his arm. He looks her in the eye and wraps it around his finger. Before the credits roll, he takes her hand and they leave.

They fold into each other to hide their faces from the wind. He holds her tightly, threading his arm behind her waist to steer her round corners. Everyone gives way to them. Sithara is so used to stepping aside that holding ground makes her giddy.

Paul buys a twelve-pack of beer and they go to his flat. A fire is burning bright in a small brazier. He introduces Sithara to three flatmates, firmly correcting the girl when she mispronounces her name. Sithara tries to get close enough to the fire to be warm without singeing her hair.

She drinks her beer, pretending she likes it.

Did you grow up in Dunedin? she asks Paul.

I grew up in Geraldine.

Is your family still there?

My dad is. He bristles, clenches his jaw. My mum died when I was ten.

My dad died when I was fifteen, Sithara says.

She thinks about Appa's face. All these years and her grief still feels like hitting water, belly first. Weeks, sometimes even months will pass without tears, and then a Sunday afternoon in her flat will tug at what was buried and she will crank the volume on her stereo so that Linda and Steve don't hear her sobbing.

Paul says that he is sorry for her loss and takes her hand. His hard calluses stud her palm. They drink and watch the fire. Ash floats onto their clothes and the heady smell of it settles and sticks.

After they fuck, Paul is breathless.

I only came fast because you're so beautiful, he says.

He kisses her neck and she trembles, shimmers with joy. She wonders if she has become a woman now. If womanhood is somehow tied to taking the breath out of a man.

She tries to smile in a way that is nonchalant, that gives the impression of being vaguely aware of the beauty he is referring to, rather than shocked. Paul drinks from a glass of water and stretches. He looks so peaceful. She can hardly believe her own ability to make someone happy by doing so little.

She pulls her clothes back on and goes to find the bathroom, passing a dining room table with some dirty plates piled on top of one another. Broken glass sits in the corner, swept but never tossed. Used cans and bottles are lined up in tidy rows. The others are still talking by the fire.

You're leaving? Paul asks. He lets himself into the bathroom while Sithara is halfway through peeing. She tries to act as though she is not embarrassed of her skinny legs, her awkward squat as she rises to dab herself dry, the wriggle she has to perform to get back into her pants. She can't remember anyone ever watching her go to the toilet.

My brother is coming in the morning.

She should have called Suri this evening. She has every other time he's come to see her. But she's never had a date before. She's allowed to enjoy her night without worrying about her brother. She reasons away her unease.

When Paul looks at her it is like he can see through her clothes to the skin beneath. Beneath the skin to her bones. It wouldn't really matter if she was naked or not. Perhaps this is what real intimacy feels like, another person bearing witness to every moment. Sithara washes her hands and looks around for a towel. Paul offers to take her home and she settles for wiping wet hands on her pants.

For herself, Sithara has not pictured romance. She has felt desire and acted on it, briefly, with one of her flatmate Steve's friends the same week she moved in, to get it over and done with. It didn't feel like much of anything. Overall she has had little to do with men she is not related to, few interactions with which to build a vocabulary.

Sithara learned quickly that boys at school were interested in her only as a way to get close to the white girls. She was useful because she was the best kind of access. No girl could possibly think that the man pursuing her via Sithara was interested in Sithara herself.

Don't tell your brother I dropped you home at 1 am. Paul gives a shouty, uneven laugh.

She kisses Paul's ear, smiles at him, moves closer in the car until she is wrapped around his arm, resting her head on his chest.

Suri's only seventeen. I don't discuss my sex life with him.

Was it just sex then?

Of course not, she says.

When they reach her house, Sithara opens the door to leave but the handle is jammed. She tries it again and turns back to Paul.

He draws her in, caressing her, one hand on her neck, the other at the base of her spine. The smell of smoke still lacing their collars. He kisses her again.

He kisses her like he knows exactly what he wants. Sithara's mind floats away from her body. It feels so good to be handled, to be contained entirely. He unlocks the car door with the flick of a switch.

How come you didn't call last night? Suri asks, turning his head to look at Sithara.

He is driving her car from the train station to the cafe. It is less than a kilometre. She thought he would be nervous but he seems relieved to be driving with someone that isn't Amma.

Annah, focus. Suri makes a face at the road but stops talking.

Just before they reach the cafe he stalls. They bunny-hop across an entire intersection while station wagons and utes honk around them. Suri starts laughing after his third unsuccessful attempt, so Sithara boots him out to get them safely to the other side. They must have been a sight, Suri wheezing with laughter, propping himself up on the bonnet, Sithara urging him back into the car, scolding him like their own amma.

Sitting opposite each other they eat hot cheese rolls, dipping the crusty buttered ends in tomato sauce. At his feet, Suri has a large bag for the weekend, full of food for the freezer. Amma has packed curries in ice-cream containers and wedged three tins of baking around them. If Sithara paces herself, she can just about make Amma's food last a month.

Sithara checks the cafe in case Paul or his friends have wandered in. There's no reason to expect they would, but running into people is just part of living in a place as small as Dunedin. She uses the back of her teaspoon to check her hair.

Why are you so happy? she asks Suri.

He shuts his eyes tight and smiles with all his teeth. It's not illegal anymore.

What's not?

Being gay, in New Zealand.

I saw it on the news. I didn't know it ever was.

Of course you didn't. He takes Sithara's last cheese roll off her plate.

How's Amma? she asks him.

She's started watching *Coronation Street*, so she doesn't bother me at night anymore.

The thought of Amma watching TV alone, head halfway down the couch, white socks loose around her ankles, makes Sithara sad.

I think it might be a good time to tell her, Suri says.

Sithara still feels the heat of Paul's eyes on her. Suri stacks their plates on top of one another and pushes them to the end of the table for the waitress.

It's real now. It's too good an opportunity to miss. Suri says.

He's looking at Sithara with such hope. Even though he's almost eighteen he still has a child-face, bright and clean. Maybe he will always look this way.

Suri, I don't think she's going to be able to handle it.

Handle what? I'm not hurting her.

You know what I mean.

Suri pushes his cup hard, sliding it right past the stacked plates and onto the floor. It makes a loud, anxious crack when it lands.

Sithara bends to pick up the pieces. She and Suri sit in silence.

I just don't want her to get mad at you.

Suri's face has fallen. He probably counted on her support, but thinking ahead is her job as his big sister.

You really don't understand, do you? Suri says woodenly, staring at the table.

Sithara shakes her head. I do, Suri, she says. Has he forgotten the last time Amma got angry at them? The way the mountain shook? What it cost? Her rage has no limits.

She wonders what Paul would tell him to do. If he would suggest that Suri tell Amma the truth and face the consequences. Or if he would support her telling him that the best thing is to move quietly.

Even sitting alone with Suri it is as though Paul is beside her. This man she knows nothing about but feels so close to already. Only half of her is here with Suri. The rest is in shadow, waiting for Paul's touch to pull her back into the light.

Josephina
1957, Singapore

Josephina adds half an hour to her walk home from school to idle beside the Singapore River. It is not a clean or safe place for a sixteen-year-old girl. But families live their lives in the open here and Josephina enjoys watching them do so.

She stares at the houseboats. She loves their impermanence and delicacy. A woman moves around inside one purposefully, a baby strapped to her chest, sleeping. Their home looks happier than hers ever has.

She tries to walk the tight streets without drawing attention to herself. They smell of fish heads and the meaty scent of sweat. She stops to watch a hawker deep-frying balls of banana mashed into dough with flour and sugar. Men eat their lunch with their hands, on low stools squashed up against the wall of a building, leaving only a slim pathway for people to trot through.

Josephina needs to be home shortly to start dinner, but there is peace here, observing from the sidelines. She leaves when the sailors start calling out to her to come aboard.

Josephina's father left them with more debt than the house was worth. After he disappeared, they moved. They sold the house, the furniture, the land. The three of them piled into a two-bedroom apartment on Serangoon Road. Josephina tried to bring the grey cat but she was frightened of the cars and the people. She bounced out of Josephina's arms and melted into the crowds around a North Indian restaurant, off to start another life. Their new home is closer to the hospital and to Josephina's school, but they live above a brothel.

Josephina is sixteen, engaged to no one, and in her final year of school. All of these things fill her with pride. She is old enough to take care of herself and of Pātti. It is clear now that her father was the only thing tethering her mother to the family. She pays the rent, leaves money for groceries, eats the food Josephina cooks, but there is not a single moment that Josephina suspects her mother's feelings about her have changed. If not for Pātti, she is sure she would have been kicked out.

Kanthi Mummy, their neighbour, is also the landlord. She runs the 'massage parlour' their apartments sit on top of. There are chairs outside, massage beds in case the police come knocking for some reason other than patronage.

Waiters and hawkers who visit during their short breaks get neck rubs from pretty girls. Occasionally, they sidle into the space that is separated into different compartments by screens and sheets, which functions as a clean, moderately expensive whorehouse.

Josephina has grown into the beauty she was always told she would be. And despite the stuttering fear that presses against her chest and throat, she stands up straight and doesn't flinch when she looks in a mirror. Often she is lonely. She has little to comfort her other than Pātti. Her consolation, the thing Josephina reaches for on the nights she can't sleep, is the memory of exacting revenge for what was done to her.

Josephina avoids people's eyes unless absolutely necessary. This is effective only to a point. Men care solely about the parts of her they can possess. As she walks down the street cars stop and open their doors, inviting her in. In crowds, hands find their way around her waist or under an elbow. She abandoned the friends she had at school as their fathers or brothers tried, one by one, to corner her. Josephina has developed a sixth sense for whom she can and cannot trust. She knows by the sound of someone's voice if they will be kind to her. It is an instinct she has honed, polished clean.

Josephina has been handled more times than she could ever count, but for six years she has managed never to be alone in a room with a man.

—

Josephina arrives home to Pātti. She keeps the curtains closed; the light hurts her eyes. There is a small platform in the lounge she has taken to sleeping on because she snores like a train. Josephina has tried many times to give Pātti the bedroom, but hours later Pātti will creep back into the lounge and adjust her bony limbs next to Josephina.

Today Pātti is sitting up on her little mattress, eyes wide, chewing the betel and looking at her hands. When she sees Josephina she smiles, a small drop of juice falling from her rusted teeth to her chin. Josephina wipes it away and kisses Pātti on the cheek. She is close to ninety now. She moves a little slower, hears with some difficulty, but still glows like embers when she sees her granddaughter.

Put these somewhere your mother won't find them, says Pātti, pressing her immense ruby earrings into Josephina's hands.

Aiyo, Josephina whistles. They are heavy, solid 22K hoops, with small domes hung with rubies in the shape of tears.

What will you wear to church? She passes them back.

My ears need a rest. Pātti tugs at her ragged lobes, plants the earrings in Josephina's hands and closes her fingers around them.

They sit side by side, Pātti chewing and spitting with gusto. Josephina realises she's the new owner of the most valuable items in the house. Her mother would kill her if she knew.

Go see your friends, darling, Pātti says, folding down onto her mattress.

Josephina gets up and tiptoes to her bedroom, tucking the earrings into a handkerchief and placing them under her pillow. She tries not to think about the significance of Pātti giving her an inheritance, but it knocks away in her mind regardless.

Josephina couldn't eat for two weeks after her father disappeared. Her stomach was full of fear. Pātti brushed her hair with special tenderness, though she did not ask a thing. She was desperate to tell Pātti, to tell anyone, to share the dread and triumph of the moment. But the more people she told, the harder it would be to escape. Josephina wasn't even sure she had words for what Mr Brooks did to her. And if she couldn't explain his crime, how could she justify hers?

She splits the curtain in the living room ever so slightly to see outside. It is still light. Laundry hangs from the window on long poles. Her mother's uniform, Josephina's school smock, one of Pātti's saris. Kanthi Mummy's petticoats hang close by – made to measure, longer than usual. Blouses billowing like a ship's sail. Tiny, lacy underthings the girls give her to wash. Josephina has never before considered that hanging clothes look like hung people.

At six foot two, Kanthi Mummy is the largest woman Josephina has ever seen. She has forearms the size of Josephina's whole torso and wears her hair in a skinny plait that stops ten inches off the floor. Her baby hairs frizz out in a grey halo. She has three gold teeth that twinkle when she smiles.

The day they moved in, Kanthi Mummy's eyes widened at the sight of Josephina. She walked up to her and slowly took in every inch. Then she pressed her palms together in prayer and lifted Pātti up the stairs with her big arms like she was a young bride. She asked no questions, she accepted the first rent would be paid late; she took three women living together without a husband or father in her stride. Josephina had a sense that Kanthi Mummy could break a person as easily as she could fix them.

She employs six women, which is a lot by Serangoon Road standards. There is a Muslim girl named Raana, who leaves her niqab on, even in the back room, whether out of shame or for anonymity, Josephina doesn't know. There is a Tamil girl – Madhvi, who Kanthi Mummy calls Thangachi, and four Chinese women: Margaret, Jing, Yuzhen and Flowers, who are sisters.

According to Flowers, she was given her name by Kanthi Mummy when she stepped in to try and get work as a masseuse. Her jasmine and marigold perfume was so enticing she was told her qualifications wouldn't be necessary, and hired on the spot. Flowers brought her eldest sister Margaret the next day.

Kanthi Mummy was taken by Margaret's sloping lips, shiny hair and docility. She was the one who let slip about there being two more daughters in the family. Kanthi Mummy shook her head and feigned sadness. Then she pressed cash into Margaret's hand and told her to bring her sisters within the week.

Well-dressed Indian and Malay businessmen frequent the place. Most of them favour Margaret. Big old towkays strut into rooms without picking a girl, yelling when one isn't sent through the same minute they arrive. English gentlemen pull up in chauffeur-driven cars and inquire as to whether the only room that has a door is free. Sometimes they ask for two girls. One of them, with shoulders like a bull, leaves snarling when denied.

What Josephina likes best is to sit in the back with Madhvi and Jing. Jing has freckled irises. She sees the world like Josephina does – wide and cruel. The girls drink samshu and Josephina has tea. They listen to the American records the ex-soldiers sometimes bring and laugh about things their clients ask them to say. When she's with the girls, Josephina feels free.

Once there was a man whose affairs made the thin walls shiver and crack. Josephina watched Kanthi Mummy tap the door with the tip of a machete until a squat Englishman opened it. He looked at Kanthi Mummy with disgust for a long, stifling moment. Margaret was in the room behind him, sitting on the bed with her arms wrapped around her knees. Josephina peeked out from behind Raana, nervous that something bad was going to happen, determined to help prevent it. Kanthi Mummy bristled. Held the machete in two hands like a cricket bat. Peeled him with her eyes.

He left without a word.

Josephina pushes aside the batik cloth that hangs over the doorway. Her eyes ache from the light of a lived-in room. Its walls have been painted green, a blanket hung on a makeshift rail to wall it off like a curtain. It does nothing to muffle sound, but Josephina is so used to the moans and profanities now that she hardly notices.

An English-style table sits in the middle, eight chairs wedged around it. Elegant glass tumblers stolen from Raffles Hotel are smug beside chipped Japanese teacups and pots of tea.

Kanthi Mummy sits alone smoking a pipe and squinting into a small notebook.

Now what time, Josie? she says, gesturing to the clock on the wall. Sit, sit, sit. She pushes the chair opposite out with her foot and pours Josephina a cup of tea.

Jing walks in wearing a pink satin robe and smoking a long cigarette. Her face is framed by a short Rose Chan-style bob; she twists in hot rollers whenever the parlour is empty. A faded dragon tattoo snakes around her forearm. Jing has a young daughter, Trinity, who lives with her in Chinatown. Josephina sometimes wonders if Jing is thinking of her own daughter when she looks at her.

Jing winks at Josephina and sets a paper bag of curry puffs down. Jing and Madhvi were the girls Josephina met first. She saw them sitting around the table in lacy slips, slouched, playing cards and drinking from short tumblers like men. She had never seen women look like that. Like they lived a hundred lives at once. Like they sprinted through the usual events – marriage, death, children – and left to look for more.

This afternoon she can hear what sounds like Margaret a few rooms away. She is busy with one of her regulars, a man who pays her extra to scream at him. Breathless strings of insults about his mother, his wife, his manhood. After she tends to him, Margaret always returns with a smile.

Margaret and Raana often work together. Josephina doesn't know exactly how or why. She assumes that seeing Raana unclothed is something men pay a kind of a premium for. Perhaps she leads an entirely respectable life outside of this and is picky with her clients because of it. Maybe Margaret protects her from them. Maybe she keeps her face hidden even while naked. The two of them usually arrive and leave together. They are often sitting close, murmuring to one another. Ranna's voice is husky; Margaret's lips are like petals at her side.

Josephina blows on a curry puff. They are steaming hot, crunchy on the outside and fluffy in the middle. Jing pours chilli sauce on hers and does the same to Josephina's without asking. Inside her chest, Josephina's heart is thawing out.

Listen, I don't mind the fat ones, lah, but you can't give me three in a row, Mummy, Jing complains. She jabs the air with her cigarette as she talks and purses her lips to blow the smoke away from Josephina.

Kanthi Mummy smiles and shakes her head. You don't want the fat ones? Don't be so delicious.

Madhvi enters, yawning. She is short like Josephina, with long silky hair she dyes auburn with henna. She can't be much older than twenty. Kanthi Mummy speaks often of her hatred of madams who employ teenagers and of clients who ask her for them. But Josephina suspects that Madhvi wiggled her large breasts and slim hips through the cracks. Today she sits next to Josephina, leaning her head on her shoulder.

You're working all night, Thangachi, Kanthi Mummy says, frowning. Madhvi waves a yes at her.

Josie, you know I have some men who would pay just to take you out? No funny business, no nothing, just time spent with a pretty girl, Kanthi Mummy says. She puts a shot down in front of Madhvi, and after staring at the bottle for a second, pours one for herself. Josephina shakes her head but smiles so she doesn't seem ungrateful. For years Kanthi Mummy has been more comfort than her own mother.

She's sixteen, Mummy, Jing says, scowling.

This is why I say no *nothing*, you hear me? Kanthi Mummy shoots back.

She wrenches the blanket aside and walks out, her head

brushing the ceiling. Madhvi chuckles and pours samshu for the three of them, settling a big one in front of Josephina. All this time they have avoided giving Josephina alcohol and she has never asked. She doesn't care for the smell of it, is already sure she won't enjoy the taste, but she loves the swagger it gives the girls. The way they stand up straighter, speak more carelessly. It is so sweet to watch women live at the edge of themselves.

Josephina takes a sip and her throat closes. She coughs violently while Madhvi cheers. Jing smacks her back hard and rubs her shoulders, making gentle shushing sounds. Josephina flinches. This tenderness hits harder than the drink did. She still has to remind herself to breathe every time someone touches her. Pātti is the only person who ever holds Josephina.

Madhvi throws her shot back and reaches her arms to the floor, stretching her legs to ready herself for hours of work, as the evening rolls slowly in.

✦

Six years ago, the night it had happened, Josephina didn't leave her room. The front door closed and there was silence for hours. She stayed flat on her back in bed like a doll. Her mother came home and helped Pātti to bed. Josephina listened to her mother pacing round and round the good room, noticed how hollow her footsteps sounded without the rug to cushion them. She waited for her father to return with the police, but he never did.

The next morning her mother was waiting in the kitchen. She stood by the sink, arms folded, nostrils flaring. Josephina didn't expect anything as human as comfort from her mother, but her icy anger pierced Josephina's cheek like a fish hook. She found she still had rage left to meet it. She glared back.

Your father has left instructions, her mother said finally. We're selling the house.

She jabbed a finger into Josephina's collarbone and held it there, skewering her to the wall.

What did you do, Azab?

Josephina walked forward, driving the finger deeper into her chest, staring her mother down.

Me? What did *you* do?

Josephina's mother gasped.

Her face ignited with guilt. Her finger dug in for one moment longer and then released Josephina, a bruise already forming. She looked away, her lips curling into a sneer, trying to summon some kind of contempt, even as she surrendered.

✦

Jing and Madhvi drink spirits like water, but after only two, Josephina is quite out of sorts, the alcohol reacting to the stores of fear and anxiety in her stomach. She staggers up to the apartment, straight to the bathroom. She kneels beside the metal tub and drapes her hair into it.

Affection for affection's sake from anyone other than Pātti unsettles her. She rubs shampoo into her roots and lifts unsteady bowls of water to the nape of her neck, pouring them over her hair. The ends float to the top of the water like rubbish.

Josephina has spent years prodding around in her heart for a scrap of guilt. She has found nothing. It took some time – a year, maybe two. But after the fog cleared, after the salty horror and disgust left her body and the shame of being ten years old and no longer a virgin replaced it, she accepted she would do the same thing again.

Josephina still wakes at the lightest sound, clawing the top sheet away from her neck, in her dreams mistaking the thin cotton for a leather belt.

The front door clicks open. She hears the chime of bangles falling onto the dresser. Her mother often shuts herself in the bedroom until Josephina and Pātti have eaten and gone to their beds. Sometimes it will be weeks before she sees her mother's face. She stays where she is, head hanging over water, tracing patterns in the soap scum with her fingers.

You'll never guess what Kanthi Mummy said to me today, Josephina calls to Pātti. She reaches into the cupboard to pull out a five-kilogram sack of rice, smiling, anticipating Pātti's cackle when she hears. Her scornful granddaughter, posing as a charming date? No doubt Josephina would scoff at everything he said, growl if he even tried to open a door for her. It would be almost comical.

Pātti doesn't respond. She is sleeping so deeply she's not even snoring. She doesn't usually sleep this long in the afternoon. Josephina looks directly at Pātti for the first time and drops the rice. She hears the same buzzing sound she once thought signalled her own death. It rocks her whole body.

Pātti is lying on her side, on top of the blankets. Her hands are clasped under her chin. Eyes open, looking at nothing, mouth locked shut. Her skin is the colour of cardboard. Josephina kneels, needing to get close to her.

She tries to think before she allows herself to feel. Her mother is still in her room. She will have to tell her. They have barely any money for funeral arrangements. Maybe they will ask the church for help. Josephina could sell one of the earrings. She accepted them so naively; she knew what it meant but not that it would be so soon. It is too soon. She is scared to touch Pātti when she looks so changed. But she can't bear not to.

She crawls across the floor and presses two fingers to Pātti's forehead. Her widow's peak is as proud as ever. Her skin is cold. She closes Pātti's eyes. Whispers a prayer under her breath, asking for her safe passage, for peace. She feels certain that no one is listening, but Mother Mary was, once. Then she lies facing Pātti and clasps her own hands, mirroring her position exactly.

This is how the two of them stay, old and young, dead and living, in the dark, hollow flat. A thought running through Josephina's head finally brings with it the guilt she thought she wasn't capable of feeling. Pātti was alone when she died.

Annie
2018, London

Suri passes Annie a freshly made pita. It is thick and fluffy and filled with halloumi and grilled vegetables. He points to a jar of yellow-green chillies in oil. He eats like Gran – loudly, like nothing makes him happier.

Annie begins to tell Suri story after story from her life. She shakes her past onto the table like Scrabble tiles. Gym, moving to Christchurch, leaving Christchurch and getting into the film industry. She performs her history. He laughs at the parts Annie also thinks are funny.

When he says certain words, like 'nicely', slowing down the syllables and rounding off the end, when he flicks his wrist, turning his palm up and out, he brings Annie's mum into the room. It is brief, but she appears fully, staring at Annie through Suri's eyes.

After only a few hours sitting with her uncle, there are some things Annie feels she knows for sure. Suri is a good listener. He is gentle. Like all funny people with handsome smiles, he is a little thrilling to be around.

But her presence makes him uneasy. He fidgets while they talk. Annie can't stop looking at his shiny head. She wonders if he fought it. If he held on, praying, while the top slowly thinned. Or perhaps he shaved it clean and never looked back. If she knew this she might know him.

Around 4 am she asks Suri about Paul.

Did you meet him?

Suri smooths his forehead.

Your father? he says.

Annie nods.

Suri avoids Annie's eyes. I did.

Did you like him?

No.

Annie watches him. Again he is uncomfortable. She changes the subject, not wanting to push Suri too far, too soon.

And Appa? What was he like?

Your mum hasn't told you?

She's tried, but she gets too sad.

Suri stares at her, his gaze momentarily hard. Your mum has never told you about our appa?

A lump grows in Annie's throat.

He was brave. He was never angry. When Appa walked into a room everyone in it became happy. I thought the grief would get easier, but it doesn't.

Suri stops, looks at Annie, shrugs. They allow the silence to ripple between them. She thinks of the photo in his spare bedroom and knows that she has missed Suri for her whole life.

I wish you had been able to meet him, if only to see him and Amma together. There were so many parts of her I never saw again after he died. Really, it was like we all just forgot how to love each other. Amma was never very good at it, but when he died it felt like her love did too. I hated Amma for that.

Annie has never heard anyone talk about Gran like this. How could you hate Gran? she asks.

Suri pulls his phone close to him and checks the time. You need to go to sleep or you'll never get back on track.

Annie nods, worried again that she has overstepped.

I'll be here, he says.

Annie

1997, Hamilton

Hamilton in the nineties is a lot like Hamilton in the eighties. And not too dissimilar from Hamilton in the seventies. The houses on the river all look as though they were built by people who had just made money. Dentists, plastic surgeons, one or two software designers who weren't sure how much richer they were going to get, who could have waited a couple more years and bought in Auckland. The town centre has the air of a party that just finished, one where everyone cleaned up badly. It does feel like something happened here once, but nobody remembers what it was.

Annie sits in the backseat of her grandmother's car, staring at the sun. It is whiter than a lemonade popsicle, pure enough to clean her. At first the sun's blazing arrogance burned her eyes, but now it feels normal. Her little head twists as they turn corners, trying not to break contact; she is counting seconds so she can tell her mum how long she looked. She'll tell her that all grown-ups know nothing because looking at the sun doesn't hurt, it just makes you realise how grey everything else is.

Gran is driving fifteen kilometres under the speed limit, listening to National Radio. Men in big cars overtake her, thinking size will protect them, unaware that Gran's scowl is vicious enough to break the skin. They are driving beside the Waikato River, passing houses with flat roofs and too many windows.

Sometimes the river is exciting to Annie. She likes to imagine what it must look like down there. Thin beams slicing through the thick brown top of the water, illuminating fields of moss and seaweed. Everything tinged with green, boulders the current passes over like a veil. Underwater caves and baby Maui floating, wrapped in his mother's strong hair like they learned about in school. She imagines herself becoming part of the river, diving in and never stopping, swimming straight to the bottom with her own hair streaming behind, the only part of her reaching back to the surface.

Annie is seven years old. She has dirty knees sticking out of her school culottes and a black eye. She has a mullet, with a fringe she cut herself, long enough to hide the fried-egg ears people always tell her are big.

Annie is not especially short, but she is thin in a way

that is particular to children only, startling and temporary. Her stare unhinges people. It's one of a few social cues she has not picked up on. When to look away, when to look with less intensity. She only knows how to give all of her attention at once.

Annie got her black eye a week ago, running away from the living room. She was too distracted to move her feet properly and she collided with the stair's sharp wooden edge. All of the feeling in her body seemed to travel to her cheek and vibrate there, ringing like an alarm. Her vision went blurry and she screamed.

It was Gran who came for her. Annie didn't even know Gran was in the house, but suddenly there she was, examining her. Gran was so warm. She smelled of peppermint and cloves. She held Annie's matchstick body, kissed the good side of her face and told her she was going to be okay. Then she scooped her up and hummed a lullaby in her ear, drowning everything else out.

While the pain of that day has faded, Annie's black eye somehow looks worse. It squats on the side of her face. Annie studies it constantly, checking its progress. She is disgusted but also protective, like it's her pet. Or a work of art, puddling around her left eye, a brutal purple in the centre, spreading out into blue, red and even yellow at the edges.

The yellow is the worst part. It looks as though her skin is rotting underneath. She has become quite used to grown-ups recoiling from the sight of it, trying to sew their faces back into a smile.

Annie is familiar with pain. Once she bit her wrist so hard she broke the skin. She refused to tell Gran what had happened, which sent Gran into a frenzy. She made Annie get rabies shots. Another time she pulled hundreds of hairs out of her head, leaving a bald patch above her ear. This was much more effective and easier to hide.

The space inside Annie's head fills up too quickly. She is already more than half-full to begin with, but people keep topping her up. At school she empties her entire pencil case before using anything inside it, and lays her pens the exact same distance apart. She orders them by colour, size, or usefulness. And only when they are perfect does she return to the room. This is how she makes the world simmer down.

When Gran picked her up from school today, she told Annie they were going to The Office. This is what the two of them call the legal firm where her mum works. Annie tried tossing her backpack to the ground in protest, knowing the detour would mean she would miss her daily half-hour of cartoons, but Gran just threw her handbag too, which made Annie laugh.

The news on the radio of someone called Versace dying makes Gran sigh and kiss her teeth. Annie asks why he was shot.

He wasn't shot, he was assassinated, Gran says.

Annie pulls her eyes off the sun, black spots blooming behind her eyelids, and reaches out to touch her grandmother's hair. Her salt and pepper curls are soft in Annie's hand.

Why was he assassinated?

He was a queer, Annie, Gran says, making the radio louder as if to shut Annie up.

Gran wears thick-rimmed glasses and she always knows when Annie is lying. She can sense Annie unwrapping the tinfoil from a Ferrero Rocher hidden at the back of the cupboard, or winding up some forbidden lipstick, breathing mist gently onto her own reflection, inching the stick closer and closer. Her voice will float in a warning from another room and devastate Annie before she can be 'sophisticated'.

Annie's mum is sophisticated. She is the most glamorous person Annie has ever seen. Her skin is dark like gold under the sun; her heavy black hair flows to her waist and tickles Annie's nose and eyes when they are close; she wears skirt suits and thick hoops and draws brown lipliner on in the rear-view mirror, long fingers tapping the steering wheel.

Four days ago, her mum climbed into Annie's bath and cried. Annie knew she had been to the police station, but they didn't talk about why. Annie was experimenting with the water. She let it run, got it as hot as possible, and then twisted the handle. Scalding water poured onto her vagina.

It hurt more than any other part of her body she'd tried, so much she started sweating.

Her mum crashed in and Annie shot backwards away from the tap, and watched as she pulled her dress off in one go. She left her underwear and socks on and lowered herself down in front of Annie.

Annie wrapped her arms round her as far as she could, rested a cheek on her spine and told her everything was going to be okay. Loose tendrils of her mum's hair spilled down. Like the arms of a jellyfish, it left little electric charges on Annie's skin. There were deep bruises all over her mum's back in the shape of flowers. A garden of purple and black worming across her torso. She looked broken. Annie had never seen anyone heave with tears like this.

Gran parks her red Daihatsu in the guest park of the law firm. The building is ten storeys high and dusty brown with fat ridges running rings around the outside. She frowns at the double doors that guard the entrance, her shoulders hunched.

In Sri Lanka, Gran was a teacher. Annie likes to picture her in a sari, riding to school on an elephant, telling students off while leaves burst in through open windows and monkeys fight over fruit stolen from schoolbags. Real stories about Colombo get mixed in with dreams.

She tells Annie they will have to wait in the car because

Annie is too young to go inside. Annie asks again about the designer who was shot and Gran starts to tell her about the most beautiful woman in the world, Naomi Campbell. She tells Annie that Versace's symbol was Medusa, a gorgon with snakes for hair. Born out of violence, with eyes that turned people to stone.

Annie asks question after question.

Why was she turned into a monster?

Was she pretty?

What is rape?

What did the snakes on her head eat?

Annie is so in love with Medusa that she jumps when her mum clicks her nails on the window. Her Mum tries to give Gran advice on the best route to take to the police station, and the two of them start arguing about it. Annie gets her schoolbag and stands between the two of them on the asphalt, unsure what to do with her hands.

Annie trots to keep up. Her mum has only one speed and she doesn't like supermarkets. She always races through the shopping, sticking to a list, allowing Annie maybe one improvisation outside of it.

But places full of food always feel like a treat to Annie. She likes the glossy fruit piled high. She likes fat glass bottles of apple juice and plastic bags of dinner rolls. She likes everything in its place, gleaming. She loves when there are kids outside running a sausage sizzle. She stands in the car park while Gran loads the car, biting into a perfectly charred sausage, thin white bread sticking to the roof of her mouth.

Last time she was here she wiggled her eyebrows at Gran and then dove into the pick and mix. Gran distracted the supermarket attendant by asking why there were no curry leaves in the produce section and Annie caught up when her pockets were full, sliding Gran one cashew for every three she fed herself.

They turn out of the dairy aisle and Annie is overwhelmed by stale perfume. She grabs her nose in protest and sees a white woman on the other side of the freezer staring at them, wringing the handle of her shopping trolley. Annie's palms start sweating. She tries to paste her fringe over her black eye.

In the confectionary aisle Annie stops. She needs to brush her hands over the gold and purple packaging. She presses a Flake close to her nose so she can smell the chocolate inside, and sighs. She loves how chocolate always smells warm. There's no Cadbury at Gran's. No takeaways, no chips, barely even pre-made sauces. Her friends eat two-minute noodles for dinner. But meals are always an entire production at Gran's house. Hours of cooking, five or six dishes on the table.

Annie bends down to push her fingers deep into the bags of fun-size chocolate bars until she feels the whirr of a presence behind her. A large man is standing very close.

The shock of it makes her heart beat so fast it takes Annie a second to hear what he is saying.

He is asking if the brown woman with the hair is her mother. His voice is like a fire alarm. He's wearing black cargo shorts and a white polo with stains on the collar, and he falters when Annie stares back at him without blinking. She holds her ground, drilling him with her gaze, levelling him out.

He says, Sweetheart? That eye of yours doesn't look good.

Vibrations start ringing behind Annie's black eye, making her whole head pulse. The man reaches out a hand.

She jerks out of his grasp and runs, her bare feet slapping the linoleum. Fluorescent lights seem to scurry both above and below her, rivers of white. She remembers falling on the stairs – every time she lifts her feet, she braces for the floor to rear up like a wave. Shelves loom, stone-coloured meat, flesh that looks nothing like the animal it came from. Annie wonders if cows blink. She thinks about how every cow is made of practically the same ingredients as her.

She wheels around the aisle of baking things and sees her mum's back at the checkout. The white woman from the freezer is there. She is talking fast, sucking the moment clean, rolling it around in her mouth like a cherry stone. Her mum's hair has separated into coils and twisting lengths, making her larger than anyone else. She is still holding her trolley like it's a normal day.

A security guard stands close by, shifting his weight from

side to side; the young checkout operator holds the phone at her station to her ear, wrapping the cord around her finger.

Annie starts to walk towards them, crossing no-man's-land between the grocery aisles and the checkouts. Her shoulders grow hot from the eyes of the other customers. They are staring at her mother, at Annie's face. She gets bruises all the time, but this is the only one she's worn the weight of.

The woman says, Whose child is she?

She's my daughter, her mum replies.

The security guard has a calm voice. He addresses Annie directly, crouching down to her level.

Love, we're all just a bit concerned. He trails off.

He seems nice. Annie turns to the checkout operator and smiles. I fell on the stairs, she says.

She remembers the chocolates still in her hand and puts them on the sliding black strip of the checkout counter. Annie wonders if you feel someone else's pain when you cause them hurt, if there is a link between the person yelling and the person being beaten, or if you can only kick someone in the stomach if you feel nothing at all. The woman wets her lips like the thin edges of a plastic bag and asks Annie where her dad is.

Annie says, I don't have a dad.

Her mum's hair lifts, slipping through the air towards her, but Annie flicks it off her shoulders and looks away, hot tears pricking her eyes. She runs her index finger along the pad of her thumb, pressing the nail deeper and deeper into her skin, looking anywhere but at her mum.

She picks Annie up like she is a baby, locking spindled fingers tight under her and striding away, past the angry woman, past the man from the chocolate aisle who is yelling at the kind security guard, past the checkout operator who is staring at her hands and who looks as though she is crying too, and out into the light.

Annie turns back towards the sun, but it hurts this time.

✦

Annie, her mum and Paul live in a big wooden house at the end of a gravel driveway. The ceilings are high and the kitchen is tiled with black and white diamonds that are cold underfoot. There's a spacious carport and a garden maintained by Gran with a delicate Japanese maple. Its leaves float, feathery and suspended, right in front of Gran's French doors. Annie loves to look out of the window at night and see Gran's house on the other side of the garden. She leaves a lamp on in the living room, like a lighthouse.

When Annie and her mum arrive home, Paul's car is gone. After yoghurt and mandarins for dinner, her mum says they will be sleeping at Gran's tonight.

Together? Annie asks. Sharing a bed with her mum is something she only gets to do on birthdays.

She puts her pyjamas on and folds into her mum's arms

while a single morepork calls outside. Even before her eyes close she is dreaming of Medusa. A woman so powerful her gaze alone could stop people in their tracks, a nest of snakes on her head, hissing at anyone who came close. Her Medusa is wearing white silk and the snakes tumble down her back like a glorious wig. This is where Annie is happiest – in Gran's spare room on the single bed, wrapped in a blanket of her mother's hair.

At 5 am she is woken by a car. Her dreams liquify and play at double-speed: linoleum, plastic bags writhing in the wind, the image of her own face detached from her head, lying crumpled on the floor like a scrap of paper. Her mum is wide awake, breathing fast, her hair still clutching Annie. Annie squeezes her hand and gets out of bed. Her mum sits up but doesn't stop her. She stays still. Her eyes reflect the moonlight and her hair surges, crackling.

The small living room is empty but the sliding glass door is open. It is raining. Gran stands on the slick gravel in house shoes and a sarong, raindrops polishing the tip of her nose. Annie pads out, each step testing what is stronger – her fear of the unknown, or her desire for knowledge at any cost. The scene in the driveway is lit by a police car's headlights on full. An officer is handcuffing Paul. His arms look heavy, like he has forgotten how to move them. His head jerks up. He looks past Gran, straight at Annie.

Annie remembers him coming home with a new Kelly doll for her, bringing her mum chocolates. There was one week they all talked about getting a puppy. Annie was so excited she filled a whole notebook with possible names. But the last fight hangs low and heavy over the grass, blurring everything.

Annie glares back. She can feel her gran beside her. He holds Annie's gaze until the policeman's arm casts a long shadow, guiding Paul's head into the car and shutting the door.

Annie
2018, London

In the morning, Annie tells Suri about Nia. It might be that finding Suri has freed her. It might be that waking up in a brand-new country has made her feel like a brand-new person. It might just be the fresh bread, jam and tea that was waiting for her. She tells him how she knew her relationship was a sinking ship. One morning when Annie tried to kiss her, Nia shuddered.

When Nia broke up with her she felt numb. Though she had an urge to for the first time since high school, she resisted calling her mother. She told Gran she'd had a breakup, but didn't say who with. It didn't feel right to burden Monica, her closest friend, with the news of her sad lesbian drama. Despair reached out from the ground to grab Annie by the ankles. She stamped it back into the dirt.

Annie had taken one last job, a horror movie, in which she

was short enough to play the lead actress post-decapitation, and then booked flights. Her heart wouldn't mend in Auckland.

She catches herself in the middle of describing Nia's curly hair and stops, putting down her half-eaten toast. She rests her forehead on the breakfast bar and sighs.

Your first heartbreak hurts the worst, Suri tells her.

When do you get over it?

Sometimes you don't. You just keep distracting yourself.

Well, that was the idea.

Suri stares at her. What do you mean?

Leaving. Coming here.

That's what brought you here?

She thinks about what it felt like to separate her clothes from Nia's and fold them up into her small, pathetic boxes. The shame in the months that followed. It overwhelmed her and left no room for any other feeling.

But there was so much grief before that.

Sure, why not?

She rests on her ear and looks up at him. Suri raises his eyebrow.

What was it like in Invercargill? For you and Mum.

Oh, you know, lonely. Boring. Cold.

Did the three of you do fun things together?

When have you ever seen either of them do anything for fun?

He's right of course. How strange that someone she has

never met knows the women who raised her better than she does.

Amma was furious when I left.

When you moved to London? Annie asks.

Suri stares at her without understanding for a moment and then shakes his head.

I haven't had a real conversation with her since I was eighteen. I don't even think she knows I live here now.

Annie shifts around, uneasy.

She knows. I got your address from her.

Suri snorts in disbelief.

It was written down, by hand. She definitely knows.

He rests his chin in his hands, studying Annie like he is trying to figure out whether she is a liar. She tries to not apologise, lest she look like one.

After a moment he sighs and stands up, excusing himself.

I need to call my husband. Suri leaves without noticing the ground beneath Annie has fallen away.

Josephina
1968, Colombo

Josephina sits under the banyan tree and unwraps the banana leaf holding her lunch. She has lamprais today, from the school canteen. A boiled egg, yellow rice, chicken curry, parippu, garlicky green beans and sambal. The leaves freckle golden light onto her face. She is still hard to look away from.

Each day, when class is over and her students have left, Josephina walks as fast as she can to the banyan tree. She is never alone here. Groups of friends eat lunch together, secretaries and curators from the museum come to smoke, groundskeepers and security guards move the tourists along. There are food stalls on the streets around and the roads are loud with drivers negotiating the intricate roads.

Compared to other banyans, this tree is young. It has not yet stretched parasite legs out to walk. It doesn't even take up the whole courtyard, let alone reign over a forest. But Josephina visits this tree like it is a house of god.

The first time Josephina saw the banyan she stopped still, unsure if she was dreaming. It was an illustration from a storybook come to life. Roots streamed from thick boughs, searching for their next home. The leaves were plentiful but small, frivolous in contrast to the trunk, decorating the body as well as the crown.

She knows that banyans are bridges to another world. But the first time she sat under hers, she felt closer to only herself. She wondered if this banyan was not a gate to other places, but to other parts of her life, years she just hadn't lived yet.

Josephina is twenty-seven, single, and a teacher at the Catholic girls' college in Mount Lavinia. Her colleagues often invite her to have tea with them in the staffroom. Once a week, or less if she can manage, she will trail after fellow English teacher Shalina or Vice Principal Roshan to the open-air courtyard they refer to as the staffroom.

Her workmates are cheerful and curious. They ask questions about her life and when she might get married. Josephina is stiff in comparison. She's always felt her looks are the only reason anyone can bear her personality.

When she returns from washing her hands, her spot has been taken. It's as though someone walked into her house uninvited. A man is quietly sitting just so, staring into the distance. His expression is serene, as though his mind is a thousand miles from his body.

This man's hair is blue-black and curly, so coiled and glossy it is cheerful. His face is all sharp points and angles. He wears a white shirt and pants that make his dark skin gleam. He is dressed for a funeral.

Josephina blots her palms on her orange sari and marches in front of him, scowling. He gives her a smile so effervescent that she stumbles.

You are sitting in my place, she says. She forces her chin into the air above his head.

Your place? he says. His teeth are very small, spaced slightly apart, and painfully white. He looks like an imp. But his eyes do not chew her up like most men's do. He has a gaze so steady it unnerves her. She sighs. Clearly, he has decided to be trouble. Josephina turns to leave.

It is your place, of course. I am sorry, he tells her.

The banyan's roots fall like a curtain between them. She smells lavender soap, clean and soothing. He turns and walks into the dark hallway of the museum.

Josephina tries to take her place again, but she sits left of her original spot. She cannot bring herself to share the grass he bent, that would be too intimate. The birds are louder, all the colours around her are saturated. They lend her their joy.

Singapore wasn't big enough to escape the ghosts who haunted her: Mr Brooks, Pātti, Madhvi. All of them visited. They came to her in the tip of a stranger's linen collar, in the smooth pull and swash of someone spitting betel out on the street, in the angle of a pretty girl's mouth. She learned to push them all to the back of her mind, but they are a hum that never goes away.

When she finished her schooling she stayed, working as a teaching assistant to Sister Kirby. She had some happiness still, until Kanthi Mummy and the girls were raided. Josephina was eighteen. They cracked Kanthi Mummy's jaw, broke her hip, and everything changed. Madhvi went missing. The parlour was replaced with a shoe store.

With Pātti dead and the girls gone, Josephina had nothing. Her tongue is heavy in her mouth when she thinks of the dark flat. The days became concave, moving too fast, steepling into endless evenings alone at the apartment.

She spent long nights reading in her bedroom, fantasised over ageing, over disappearing from the registry of women men try to have sex with. She dreamed about a different life, free from the curse of her youth.

Her mother met a man and moved out. Josephina talked to him once, after her mother died of a heart attack and she had to go to his flat to retrieve her things. He was weeping, far more upset than Josephina. She gathered her mother's possessions and waited for her own grief to emerge. The only thing she felt was peace.

Josephina had her mother cremated and wrote to dozens of Catholic schools in Ceylon and India in the weeks following, explaining her situation and experience, asking for a job. When she was offered a position she didn't hesitate.

Josephina tossed Singapore over her shoulder like a used tissue. The country she left was not the one she grew up in. The swamps and fields had become high rise apartments. The river was clean. The English had dwindled.

The slums of a foreign country held more appeal than the grandest estate in Singapore, so when she secured a job in Colombo, she sold Pātti's remaining earring and moved to Ceylon.

A boarding house attached to a nunnery was the only place Josephina knew she could stay as a single woman. Without strange looks or questions, without men. She was at the markets, buying house shoes and a knife, when an old man, Inesh Uncle, held pol roti out to her, smeared with sambal.

It was delicious. The grated coconut gave it a pleasing grit and weight, and the sambal was savoury, mouth-watering from lime and Maldive fish. Just as Josephina begged for the recipe, Suji Aunty bustled over. She cupped Josephina's face and spoke to her with such sweet familiarity. Josephina moved into their spare room two weeks later.

Inesh and Sujiya are siblings. Inesh Uncle is blind and in his late sixties. Suji Aunty is younger by maybe fifteen years. They are busy and generous. They give Josephina her own space and a large bedroom. They never mention hearing her yell out in the night. Josephina's nightmares have not changed much since childhood. She has learned to live with them.

The siblings are teaching her how to cook. Every afternoon when Josephina returns home, she ties her hair with a scarf, washes her hands and face, and goes to the kitchen where Inesh Uncle and his carer Ranil are waiting.

Josephina has learned how to make kottu, watalappan, maalu paan. She has learned how to gently coax appam around a pan and crack an egg right in the middle. She has started to know spices by their Sinhala names. Each morning she wakes up to a selection of fruit that Ranil has picked from the garden and arranged on a platter. Suji Aunty eats with her, rolling tiny limes under her palm and passing them across the breakfast table like precious jewels.

Recently, Suji allowed her to make the milk rice for her son's arrival home. He was to stay all weekend. Suji Aunty has never referred to a husband, but her son is a joy she speaks of often. Josephina feigned a last-minute trip with friends and left as soon as she finished cooking.

She slept at the school all weekend, locked herself in the classroom at night, walked the grounds and read during the day. She felt satisfied and warm each time she remembered slicing the milk rice into diamonds and hearing Suji Aunty's approval. She tells herself she is too busy to think about being lonely.

Memories of Pātti surface without warning. They come when Josephina is kneading dough, tying her sari, smoothing her heels with pumice stone. Although they make her cry, thoughts of Pātti are still a comfort. Josephina turns her face towards them like a fan on a hot afternoon.

+

The next day, Josephina settles herself under the banyan tree. Her sari is a dusky pink sunset. She tells herself she is not waiting for the man with the hair to return. She has pulled her hair into a low bun and her skin is gleaming from rosewater and coconut oil. She has a paper package of isso curry today, nestled in a bed of rice, some mango pickle tucked into the corner. Her fingers itch to open it. In a separate bag she has her favourite snack – peppers stuffed with tuna fish and deep fried. She got two. They sweat side by side in the bag, turning the paper translucent.

She rubs her fingers over the grass and flicks a piece of dirt off her blouse. Suji Aunty gave Josephina a smile as she snuck out the front door this morning, noticing she took twice as long as usual to get ready.

The afternoon has shrugged into evening by the time Josephina gives up on seeing him. She eats her lunch cold and gives the peppers to a barefoot child running past.

Believing he would come back for her was childish, he has probably already forgotten their meeting. Believing he could be worth waiting for is even more stupid. She folds up the bright memory of his face, as she has all painful things.

Laughter rings out. Josephina looks up to see the child she gave her snack to playing with a dog and notices she is being watched. A man is standing a polite distance away from her, resting the sole of his foot on the roots of the banyan and studying Josephina. His arms are folded and his weight is slightly back, like he is considering her, or trying to take in as much as possible.

He has broad shoulders, short legs and a pencil-thin moustache. Josephina stiffens. She readies herself for his calculated walk closer, for him to feign being casual and ask a question about her day or her plans. She tries to wipe all the expression off her face and stands to leave. He offers her a cigarette.

I'm Edward, he says.

He has a small gold ring on his pinkie with a ruby set into the middle. The gesture of a man offering to smoke with her is so surprising that although she has never had a cigarette in her life, she accepts.

Rain starts falling, sprinkling the ground between thick mottled branches. There is enough cover so that Josephina and Edward do not get immediately wet. He gives her a small smile and ashes his cigarette. She takes a few steps away, lest he get the wrong idea, and tries not to cough from hers. She notices the side of his jaw curves into his neck and ear at a pleasing angle. He's not unattractive.

She tries to inhale lightly, not wanting to cough. The cigarette tastes disgusting and the smell sticks itself immediately to her hair and her clothes and her skin. And yet, because it is right here between her fingers, she keeps smoking.

I'm an assistant curator, Edward says. My office is in the far corner there.

Josephina follows his finger to the right edge of the building. The National Museum of Colombo is snowy-white, immense, and built in the Italian style. There are generous balconies wrapping around the second floor and dark windows that she sees being washed daily. It is too pristine to be welcoming.

I've never been, she says.

He doesn't frown or try to invite her in. He just smiles. Her petticoat starts to dampen. She passes her half-smoked cigarette back to him, ducks her head and walks out into the rain.

Colombo is musky and sharply drawn on days like this. There are few footpaths, so Josephina flits along the roads for some time before getting on a bus.

When she first arrived, she thought she might blend in, but they know she is foreign before she even opens her mouth. Sana, one of her favourite students, has decided to improve Josephina's Sinhala. She started by pointing out different objects in the classroom and now she comes in each day to tell Josephina the word for a new feeling, which she expresses with her hands as much as with her earnest face.

When Josephina was a child, she believed that a terrible thing had been done to her because she was pretty. Now that she is older, she is less sure it was anything to do with her at all. Sometimes she wonders if her parents didn't know exactly what Mr Brooks wanted with her in that room. And then she remembers how her mother gathered Pātti and carried her away; Pātti, whose limbs were heavy like she had been drugged. She remembers the tidy click of her father's hand closing the door and the silence with which he met her screams, and she knows this is not true.

Inesh Uncle is listening to the radio when Josephina arrives home. Ranil is reading the newspaper. The stories leading both are of the civil rights movement in the United States. She tells them she will make ambul thiyal for supper.

Inesh told Josephina that he was born with some vision, but lost it soon afterwards. He moves swiftly and Ranil is always right behind. The two of them are close in age; Ranil seems like part of the family. Josephina has never lived in a house with staff before, but she doubts whether a friendship where one party is being paid could ever be real. He helps cook. He assists Inesh Uncle as is his duty, and she watches two old men giggle like children when they are left to their own devices.

Josephina pounds chillies, kothamalli, gammiris, suduru and goraka in a mortar and pestle. She is grinding it to a paste so that it clings to the fish. She sprinkles kaha over red fish and then throws it in the pot with a little water, coating it generously in the paste.

In the evenings, Suji, Inesh and Ranil sit in the living room and do puzzles. They listen to music. A peaceful household still feels like a kind of trick. But after two years she has not had a single argument with Suji, Inesh has never laid a hand on her, and Ranil is polite and thoughtful.

Once the fish is cooked, she carries it to the table where Ranil has set out rice, raita, poppadom and pickle. Inesh Uncle sniffs the air and smiles as he sits down to eat.

It is a whole week before she can bring herself to visit the banyan again. As she approaches the tree she sees Edward eating slices of mango from a paper bag. She starts to turn and walk away.

Hello, he says, nodding. You never told me your name.

Josephina, she says. He gives her a warm and grateful smile.

She hovers, standing awkwardly, and he stands too. They talk. At first it is nothing personal. They talk about their jobs, the weather. Edward shares a little of the lives of his two brothers and two sisters. His elder brother is brash and arrogant, the younger one dreams of living anywhere but here. His sisters are both a mystery to him but he worries that Nisha, the baby of the family, is too obsessed with wealth and appearance. Josephina wishes she had anecdotes of her own that didn't bring pain. She pictures Edward's band of siblings and realises that she wants to be a mother. She finds the conversation enjoyable. It feels like they might become friends.

She begins to look forward to meeting him in the afternoon. He brings her watermelon juice. When Dr Martin Luther King Jr is shot, they light candles and sit in silence until night comes. They swap books. She lends him *The Odyssey*. He gives her *Treasure Island*. Every so often he tries to move their interactions beyond this single location, but Josephina falls silent each time and he stops.

After a couple of months of this new friendship, Suji Aunty comes looking for an explanation.

Josephina is making love cake. Suji Aunty watches, grinning, by the sink.

Don't lie, Josie, she says, drawing her vowels out with her index finger like she is conducting an orchestra. I know there is a man.

Aunty, no, Josephina tells her, shaking her head. He is only a friend. We have the same interests. His work is close to mine. That's all.

She is telling the truth. Josephina does not feel any desire towards Edward.

This is love, ne? This is all you need. Suji Aunty wraps her arms around Josephina as she talks. Josephina tells herself not to flinch at the embrace.

Maybe Suji Aunty is right. Edward is kind. He listens. He speaks and dresses as though he comes from money. He could be a good husband.

She can hear Ranil and Inesh laughing at the puzzle they have spent three days failing to construct. Josephina pushes the cake into the oven and watches the batter melt and smooth over in the heat.

She arrives at the banyan before Edward. Today she will agree to go out with him. She wants to be part of a family. She wants a household that is happy like Inesh and Suji's. Josephina has always believed that she was the reason nothing around her worked, but it has been so easy to live since she left Singapore behind.

She knows how it will go. After they have spent some nights out, he will try to kiss her. Soon he will invite her to meet his parents and maybe even his siblings. If she impresses his sisters and his mother then things will progress.

She will bring him home to meet Inesh and Suji. They will love him, of course – he's a good Singhalese boy with a job at the National Museum.

When it comes up, Josephina will lie and tell Edward that her parents were kind, that she mourns them every day. They will probably get married right here in Colombo.

Josephina's wedding sari will be modern, white. She might even have gold lacing her wrists. With a wedding ring she will be so much more unapproachable.

When the business of marriage is done, Josephina will steel herself for the next step. She'll shut her eyes and get it over with. If she gets pregnant on the first or second try, she won't have to do it again for almost a year. She and Edward might fight; of course there will be some things they disagree over. But both of them will be too essential to the happiness of their children for the arguments to last long.

It sounds like a good life, and marrying someone she does not yet love is no great loss. Josephina is grateful she is at least able to choose, that she did not have to grow up with a father-in-law like Mr Brooks. There is so much to be thankful for.

The banyan is whispering something just out of her hearing. The air is hot and heavy; it makes it hard to think. She brushes leaves off her shoulder and scans the outskirts of the grounds for Edward.

There are two middle-aged women sitting on the grass in muted blue saris, the official uniform of clerks and assistants here at the museum. She's seen these two before. They share a bottle back and forth. They don't notice anything but each other and they barely pause for breath as they talk, like they are relishing the chance to speak in the open air. The one on the left has taken off her shoes. Perhaps they are complaining about their boss, or one of the men in charge is causing trouble, insisting they stay late, take on more responsibility and spend less time at home with their children.

There are stray dogs on the street, weaving through cars and causing drivers to stop and pound their horns. The boughs above Josephina creak out a warning. A man is walking across the grass towards her. Not Edward, but the smiling one who ruined her lunch.

He wears a light cream shirt and brown pants, and he looks at her with the same steady gaze as the day they met. Josephina stands, her bag and her book falling to the floor.

Josephina, he says, extending his hand to shake hers. I'm Ravi.

She takes it. His palms are cool. It is the first physical contact she has wanted with a man in all her life.

My brother Edward told me about the Singaporean under the banyan tree, Ravi says.

He is not looking at her like he did the day they met. There's no laugh in his eyes, no smile fluttering across his lips. He is precise, almost sombre. She becomes self-conscious of her breath and her hair and of whether she is perspiring.

I came here to find you the next day, Josephina says, in almost a whisper. I waited until it got dark.

Ravi tilts his head to the side. I came the day after that, he says. I apologise. The first time I met you was the day of my father's funeral. I did not expect to find the most beautiful woman on earth scowling at me.

She blushes. No compliment has ever made Josephina feel like this.

I'm sorry about your father. Your brother is nice. I wasn't looking for him. I've been thinking about you, she says. I'm so glad I left Singapore.

Every sentence that comes out of her mouth is a shock. She wants to split the belly of her life open like a fish and pull the guts out, placing them in Ravi's hands.

Would you have dinner with me? Ravi says.

She thinks about Edward and tries to justify her own desires – she and Edward have never promised themselves to each other. She has not met his parents. It has only been a couple of months. They have never been alone together. She saw Ravi first.

I'll speak to my brother, Ravi promises.

Josephina smiles wide. She buries her guilt, ancient and new, under the banyan tree and takes Ravi's hand.

Annie
2006, Christchurch

Every time Annie is on the bus she thinks about sex. It's where all her fantasies meet and get cut into a variety show. The trip lends itself to her arousal: the motion of the wheels, four or five different schools coming together. Fresh flesh.

The girl in front turns her head to the side to dab on lip balm. Her long red hair streams in front of Annie's face before settling, draped over the seat. Annie imagines sucking the Lucas Papaw off her lips.

The boy next to Annie is facing backwards, trying to take part in the conversation his friends are having behind them. The waistband of his shorts sits so low that she can see his underwear, the top of his butt cheek. If Annie reached out a hand she could touch the small of his back, feel the muscles under his skin, rub her thumb along his spine.

The day is hot and the stench of thirty teenagers saturates the bus. Annie is on her way to gymnastics training. She always sits three-quarters of the way down, settles herself just close enough to the back to not look like a nerd. She has few friends at her school and none on this bus.

Christchurch Boys High students keep ringing the bell so the driver has to pause at every stop. The incessant clanging drills into her brain.

Annie was on one bus where the driver got up halfway and threw the offenders off. He marched right down to the back and dragged the smuggest looking one up by the popped collar of his shirt and three of his friends had followed, howling. She hasn't seen the driver since.

Most of the Christchurch High boys live in large houses in Fendalton and Merivale. They play water polo and rugby and have tutors to help them with their schoolwork. Their parents attend school-board meetings and none of them give a shit about a bus driver.

Annie trains four days a week, to Gran's eternal dismay. Gran doesn't approve of extracurriculars. She especially hates Annie practising a sport that demands her pubescent body be clad in lycra, that makes her sweat in public and encourages people to watch her. Gran came along to one open training back in Hamilton and left halfway through, muttering to herself. Annie found her sitting in the car, no newspaper, just staring into space.

The bus slows at the leisure centre housing Annie's gym, and Shirley High boys start crowding the door. They must have just finished training. They have thick necks that open out into muscled shoulders. She can see the outline of their bodies through the thin white fabric of their shirts. Sweat makes it cling lightly to their muscles.

She steps into the crush. For one glorious moment she can't see anything other than chests and Adam's apples and chin acne, until she is spat out the other side of the crowd into hot empty air.

Christchurch is so dry it sucks the life out of her. For three months each year she has sore eyes and a scratchy throat. Everyone at home warned her it would be cold here, but the summers feel hotter. She misses Hamilton's honest humidity.

The squiggling waterslides at the back of QEII look like a giants' playground, but Annie is sixteen – too old to enjoy them without embarrassment. She walks into the Christchurch School of Gymnastics. It smells like rubber and Anti-Flamme. It smells good.

Annie is only calm when she is moving. She runs endless drills, stretches for longer than anyone else after training and tries new combinations first. Anything to put her body on the line before her mind has the chance to catch up.

Gymnastics made her realise that her awareness of her own body and of other bodies in space, was learned rather than innate. She adjusts her form quickly. She can scan the alignment of her own spine even in the air. She knows how far it is between her feet and the edge of the mat without checking. In the gym her hyper-vigilance is a skill.

She keeps her dark hair blunt. It ends at her shoulders – long enough to tie up without bobby pins, short enough not to bother her. Even if she grew it long, her hair would never look like her mum's.

Her mum's hair shifts like a mirage. It shimmers with humidity even here, like it carries its own climate. The first time Monica came over she stared, dumbstruck, as her mum's hair uncurled like fingers to hug her hello.

Annie's body is athletic. She could put this down to her gymnastics training, but she knows that's wishful thinking. She will be thick and muscled until she eventually grows old and stout, gets husky around the middle and her fingers grow wide like a builder's. She craves the tiny ankles and wrists the rest of her family shares. She blames Paul for stealing them from her.

They've been in Christchurch for a year now. Her mum left her job to start a PhD at the University of Canterbury. She decided she wanted to teach law rather than practise it. But really they moved because Paul got out on probation and was coming back to Hamilton.

Mum told Annie one night over McDonald's. They sat on the carpet in the living room with the food on the floor between them and watched *Friends*. She said Paul's probation officer rang the week before; she'd been struggling ever since to break the news to Annie.

Mum told Annie that she wanted a change, that moving to a different city on a different island would be good for them. That night, alone in her bedroom, Annie cried about leaving her friends, leaving the little house she had spent so many nights in with Gran. But she never cried in front of her mum.

She hasn't seen or spoken to Paul since she was seven years old. He got out of prison when she was ten and went back in when she was thirteen. If anyone ever asks, she says her dad is dead. She can't remember a time when she didn't hate him.

Gran said she had a bad feeling about Christchurch, despite having been there only once, and decided to move to Melbourne where her sister-in-law lives, someone her mum calls 'Maude Aunty'. Annie begged her to come with them. She made a slideshow of all the things there were to do and presented it to Gran one evening on her mum's computer. She looked up yoga classes, Catholic churches, libraries and mahjong groups. She even found an Italian film festival scheduled for a month after their move.

But Gran was resolute that there was nothing there for her. Gran and Mum started talking less and less as moving day came closer. By the time they drove Gran to the airport, Annie was passing messages back and forth like the two of them were having some sort of mother-daughter divorce.

—

Annie walks out of the women's changing rooms and into Rowey. Jonathan Rowe is a thin seventeen-year-old who works in the gym reception after school and is trying to make the squad. He lives in Burwood but goes to school in the city. At some angles his face is handsome, but only for a second. He's already too tall to ever be serious about gymnastics.

Rowey clears his throat and smiles at her.

I knew you'd be here, he says.

The skin on his arms is so colourless she can almost see the blood rushing under it. She realises with a shudder that he was waiting for her.

My friend Erin is having a party tonight. Rowey stutters a little. His parents are away. He trails off, breaking Annie's eye contact to look down at his feet.

Erin is part of the film club Annie goes to. He's chubby, funny and British. The club meets once a month at Christchurch Girls to watch old VCRs of Ingmar Bergman films, Stanley Kubrick films. Erin has always been easy to talk to. He's more sentient than the other boys at his high school, the ones Annie actually finds attractive.

Yeah, I know him, she says. I might come.

Rowey's smile makes her feel scratchy. She's always been repulsed by desperation.

The gym is starting to fill with parents and students. Most

of the girls here have been doing gymnastics since they were toddlers. Their mums hang on the sidelines for the entire session. Annie jogs around the mat, rotating her arms, feeling her body wake up.

Annie's mum sent her to a child psychiatrist when she found burn marks on the inside of her elbow. Annie was ten. She lied and said they were an accident, but her mum frowned at the even spacing. The psychiatrist's office was above a French bakery. Even now, Annie associates pain au chocolat with misery.

There were entire years Annie had just covered up, long lines of Wite-Out over the pages of her memory. She told the psychiatrist about listening out for the moment Paul got home. That it took him exactly seventy-two seconds to get inside. She told her about spending lunchtimes crying in the toilets at school. About how cutting or burning herself made her feel powerful. That it was addictive.

Watching the psychiatrist's smooth face crinkle with worry as she listened was somehow worse than experiencing everything the first time around. Annie had never understood how bad it was. She suggested that Annie be given a physical outlet. So gymnastics was the cure.

Her coach is a pretty Brazilian woman called Faris. Faris came to New Zealand when she was twenty to improve her English and work in a circus like she did in Brazil. She started coaching when she realised performers in New Zealand didn't make real money.

Annie doesn't know much else about her – only that she lives in a flat with three other women and that she finds it strange New Zealanders hide their bodies when they get changed. Faris always walks through the changing room butt naked. She starts conversations while she slowly covers her entire body with moisturiser. Her breasts are the only ones Annie has seen in real life, other than her own. Perhaps it should be strange, or sexy, but Faris's acceptance of herself in her own skin is only comforting.

The other girls in Annie's team haven't emerged from the changing rooms yet, so Faris warms up with her. Annie sees Rowey galloping around the other side of the gym and groans. Faris follows her gaze.

Don't we like him? she asks. Annie tells Faris about the party.

You should bring someone, Faris says. Bring a friend so she can watch your drinking. Watch the boys.

I won't drink. We're training tomorrow, Annie replies, frowning. She does a forward walkover and stays in bridge.

Faris shakes her head. Bring a friend anyway, she says.

It could have been that Gran's unwavering rejection of the place set a tone, but since Annie moved here, she gets it. Christchurch is different to Hamilton. It's more than just the flat emptiness of it. This place hates Annie.

At her school in Hamilton there were Samoans, Fijians,

Māori, a few other Indians. There was always Gran, with her careful, measured English, and her mum, who people twist their necks to stare at. Annie never thought of herself as foreign.

But girls at her school in Christchurch did. Her first entrance to the classroom felt like walking up the boarding ramp of a UFO. Everyone was white. There were two redheads, two brunettes and about twenty blondes, shades ranging from dyed platinum to strawberry to mousey nothingness. It was just Annie and a whole room of pale eyelashes blinking at her.

After two months she started shaving her legs. After four months she plucked her eyebrows till they were ellipses on top of her eyes. Everything was weighted differently here. Annie started falling into her own reflection.

The mothers at the gym and at school were all so hungry when Annie showed up. They slithered over one another in their attempts to get close. To touch her hard muscles. To pick at her bones. To take turns saying her last name. They drive six-seater cars and all know one another. They organise bake sales and raffles. Annie is glad her mum is different. That she is solemn and perceptive and brilliant.

She's too busy to care about the other mums. She washes Annie's pyjamas with drops of lavender oil and leaves magnesium pills on her bedside table to help her sleep. She texts Annie entire paragraphs of conversations she overhears in the library that she thinks will make Annie laugh. She listens to Annie's stories about school and gym with unwavering concentration, interrupting only to make sure she heard something controversial correctly, nodding her agreement and gesturing for Annie to continue.

Sometimes her mum falls asleep while studying, her cheek squished between the mousepad and a stack of papers, hair branching out over case notes as though it's trying to highlight things for her.

Annie and Monica walk the long way from Monica's house to Erin's party. They have been laughed at by classmates driving past them before, so if they're out after dark they avoid Memorial Avenue. Monica's family are Catholic and Polish. She doesn't have her Restricted because her parents won't let her drive. Annie doesn't have hers because her mum doesn't have the time.

Annie liked Monica as soon as they met. She was graceful, with grey eyes and a perfect side fringe. When she did speak it was in a clear, pleasantly rumbling tone. Anytime the other girls sneered at something, Monica would say it was cool.

She never elaborated, just deliberately gave her approval – to Annie carefully stretching her quads before doing PE, to the Māori social studies teacher's insistence on te reo in her class, to Bea, the only out girl at school, who showed up on the first day of term with a shaved head.

Monica's older brother Emil died in a motorcycle accident

the day he finished high school. The windowsills in her house are crowded with photographs of him, a shrine to his childhood. He was handsome, with eyes like Monica's.

Annie once found Monica's mother, Milena, sitting on the busy road in front of their house. She was reclining, staring into the sky like she hoped something would fall out of it and obliterate her. Annie can still picture her — her feet, in socks, just lying there. A woman in a station wagon swerved to avoid Milena and screamed at her out the window.

Milena wouldn't leave until Monica came out and coaxed her back inside. The expression on Monica's face was bruised. She didn't look at Annie at all. Just took her mother's arm, spoke to her firmly in Polish and closed the door behind them.

Erin's house is huge. There's a paper cut-out of a horse on the front door, clinging to a wisp of sellotape. Annie brushes its feet. They have been coloured with orange scribbles that don't meet the edges. She can already tell this is the kind of house that has a rumpus room, a fridge with an ice dispenser, probably an upstairs balcony.

Annie and Monica walk into the kitchen first. Two other girls from the film club, Lacey and Emma, are sitting on the bench. Annie imagines her gran's reaction to seeing people sitting on a kitchen bench and laughs out loud. Lacey, who is a babe, looks over. She has a cute bob, pink lip gloss, and silver rings on her fingers.

There are a couple of other girls from school. They're standing on the side of the living room like they aren't sure if they're allowed to be here, wearing long sweaters that end just above the hem of their mini-skirts. There are fifteen or twenty boys spread across sofas, around the deck, sitting on the stairs. All of them are ugly. Some look about thirteen. Annie wrinkles her nose.

So Rowey asked you out? Or just invited you? Monica asks.

I don't know, says Annie, but he was sweating the whole time.

Annie and Monica walk around counting rooms – there are three bedrooms downstairs, two more upstairs and three bathrooms. The hallway smells like feet. A sculpture mounted on the wall of the living room is just ten metal fish with holes for eyes. None of the plugs have off switches. Annie wonders if the kid who made the paper horse has ever shoved their fingers in these seething electrical portals.

There's bourbon and Coke on the kitchen bench, the tiniest bit of Midori in a large bottle of thick refracted glass, and two RTDs. Monica helps herself to one of these and wrinkles her nose at the sweetness.

You want some? she says, offering Annie the bottle.

Annie shakes her head. They stand side by side watching the rest of the party.

I'm glad we didn't dress up, Annie says. This sucks. She checks the pantry and pulls out a bag of Maltesers. Want to go back to yours and watch movies?

Stay, Erin says, leaning over the kitchen counter and smiling at Annie.

Despite herself, Annie feels her stomach swoop and dive at Erin's smile. He has improved since she last saw him. Braces off, his hair a bit cleaner. He's not exactly good-looking, but he is smiling at Annie like he wants to eat her. He waves around a plastic bottle sawn in half.

Bucky? he asks.

They make me feel sick, Monica replies.

Annie shrugs.

✦

She loses five hours. The weed turns Annie into a hot air balloon. At one point it feels like she is actually flying, like she and Erin are running down a hill. The wind is a stream of water rushing past her ears until it floods her, her brain swelling like a sponge. She sees streetlights mirrored in puddles. They look like shiny golden frogs staring at her. She fixates on the slight rash under Erin's chin, his wet green eyes. She hears Erin telling her that she is 'ethnic' then the sound of her own laughter in return, sharp and strained.

Everything happens at once but all of it is too slow. She can't catch the euphoria; she feels trapped in her own body.

She thinks of Gran and starts to cry onto the pool table. Her gran's heart-shaped face. The knuckles around her shrunken fingers. How her veins twist under her skin like roots reaching to the surface, turning earth with their urgency. Gran is a part of Annie. But she is so far away.

Franz Ferdinand blares and Annie is in a room where two boys are using a huge computer to look up pornography. The bed has six pillows. There's a door to a walk-in wardrobe, a penis filling the screen. She stuffs a handful of Maltesers in her mouth and stands swaying in the kitchen. At some point she realises she can't find Monica and begins to feel ill.

She wonders how long this feeling of running around in circles, of being circles, or everything having happened before and her having to watch it again on a loop, will last. The lights above her get turned right down and Erin's breath is hot on her neck. She becomes aware of falling onto a bed, of his hands pulling her upright. There's a *Taxi Driver* poster on the wall. Stained towels on hooks behind the door. A small wooden plaque carved with a picture of Mickey Mouse, his cartoon eyes laughing at her. She presses her hands into the duvet.

Her fingers brush the tin of an open pencil case, a protractor, compass, ruler. Erin's feet rest on the carpet, wide in white socks. Annie's hang bare, some distance off the ground. Strange. She doesn't remember taking off her shoes.

She walks herself through the floor routine Faris drilled today. Annie's first salto was loose and she landed on the outside edge of her foot. She was made to do turn after turn. She stayed an hour after training finished, tried first to catch up and then to surpass her teammates. Her abs are still clenched in phantom preparation.

Erin stares meaningfully into her eyes and rubs her thigh with his hand. He starts sucking on Annie's ear and moans a little. She can't remember the last time she said anything. It feels like being wiped with wet sandpaper. His hand skulks from Annie's thigh to her underwear. Maybe she encouraged Erin. Maybe she dangled herself in front of him like a goodie bag.

Her fingers arch out to find the sharp point of the compass. Erin reaches around her waist to pull her onto his lap. His breath is hot and furred. He'll get over it, she thinks, before plunging the point of the compass into her own hand. The pain causes her to cry out. Erin thinks she is crying in ecstasy and rushes to her zip. She slides her dripping hand in front of his face.

His breath catches. He thought she was begging for it.

Oh my god, Erin says, grabbing her hand.

I don't know how it happened, Annie lies.

Fuck, I'm so sorry. Stay there.

He grabs one of the stained towels and gently blots the ragged hole. He simpers like Annie is a wounded kitten. She lies back to avoid eye contact.

If Annie comes home this late her mum will be shocked. She doesn't get mad exactly, but her sad, silent disappointment is bad enough. Annie can't cope with being someone who upsets her mum. They hate all the same people; they're both strange here. Her mum is the only one who makes Annie feel calm, and she is the only one who makes her mum laugh.

Erin places the towel under her hand and starts fishing around in her pussy. He is pouting, holding eye contact with a self-conscious sort of awareness, as though congratulating himself.

Her blood pools on his towel, mingling with traces of sweat and shit and probably cum. Her stupid trick didn't even work. She tries to distract herself: full-in back-out, handspring, layout.

Annie actually does want to get fucked. Properly. But not by Erin. She wants to be the hottest person alive, for her body to be poison, for anyone who sees her naked to burst into tears.

The bedroom door cracks open. Rowey stands silhouetted in the light from the hallway. Rage Against the Machine blasting in the rumpus room.

Bro, what the fuck? he says.

Annie uses the distraction to grab her things. Erin starts telling Rowey that he was looking for him. He has already forgotten about Annie. She smears blood all over the duvet as she leaves.

—

Annie and her mum live in a small townhouse close to the railway tracks. It has mottled white plaster, a blue roof, and the inside is warm and sparse. Her mum said she didn't care where they lived as long as it had double-glazed windows.

She will often spread bound folders out on the wooden table in the dining room and type while Annie and Monica watch *Lost*. She brings them hot chocolate with mini marshmallows on top, melting together and forming a delicious second skin.

Annie makes it inside without flicking any lights. She tries to play the night back to herself, but so much of it is missing. She climbs the stairs, feeling guilty for leaving Monica, dizzy from tiredness. Then a light shining from the crack at her mum's bedroom door makes her pause.

She can hear low talking. Giggling. Annie's mind whirrs through all the people that would make her mum giggle at 3 am.

Gran and her mum talk on the phone occasionally, when Annie has received good marks, or a medal in gym. Annie doesn't know if her mum has made friends since they moved here and she's never thought to ask. She hears her giggle again.

There is one other possible caller. Her mum has a brother, Suri. He moved to London when Annie was a baby and as far as she knows he hasn't come home since. Annie and her mum have always been more like companions than mother and daughter. Annie has never had a bedtime, never been told she can't eat or watch something. Suri is the only thing her mum has ever really withheld from Annie.

When she has tried to ask about him, her mum has always changed the subject or left the room. She asked again just before they left for Christchurch, because her mum seemed new, flushed with excitement about the move. But Annie's question ruined the mood. Her mum snapped at her to leave it, grabbed the car keys and drove off.

When she returned after an hour it was with pink and orange tulips. She apologised for losing her temper and in a hoarse voice told Annie that Suri is the only man who really matters. Annie carried the tulips by hand onto the plane.

Annie folds her ear onto the carpet under the door. She still feels high, like her joints are loose, which is starting to piss her off.

I miss you too, her mum says on the other side of the door. Her voice is different, gooey. It leaks with something. Annie remembers how Rowey sounded when he asked her out, how she could have reached out into the air between them and plucked his feelings like a harp, could have strummed chords of desperation, lust, a strong desire for approval. This is how her mum sounds.

Annie shoves open the door. Her mum sits on the floor in an oversized t-shirt. Her hair is in the top knot she wears to shower or clean. Her eyes shine. She looks bouncy, freshly washed. She's sitting on the floor of their shitty rented flat under a twelve-dollar lamp like she is basking in the adoring light of an open fire.

Right before she clocks Annie and smashes the phone back onto its cradle, she looks like she is in love.

Who was that? Annie demands, trembling, her mouth filling with spit. Her mum stands and reaches out her arms.

Who? Annie asks again, feeling sweet milk chocolate rise up her throat. She swallows and glares at her mum, whose hair has slumped in its bun.

It was your dad, she says.

Annie spews onto the carpet. She throws up Maltesers and Coca-Cola. She heaves Erin's eggy breath and Rowey's hurt-puppy face out with her dinner. She sees stars. She sees gnashing teeth and multicoloured skin in tepid bathwater. She sees the back of Gran's head in Auckland International Airport. She sees Paul showing up at the door of their tiny safe house with a face like a riptide. She sees her mum's tenderness on the phone, sharp corners softened by joy and feels like she is seven again, running for her life up the stairs.

Josephina
1971, Colombo

Josephina knows this baby is a boy. She's fifteen weeks and everything is easy. There have been mere hours of nausea, her sweat smells the same as when she wasn't pregnant, and she has none of the terrible gassiness she had with Sithara. She wonders where he has come from.

When her daughter was born, Josephina knew she had talked with the dead. She still had the remnants of some in-between place on her. Her skin smelled of salt and metal before it smelled of baby. She looked into Josephina's eyes without blinking, as though she was saying, *There you are. I've been looking for you.*

When the three of them got home, a family for the first time, Ravi immediately fell asleep, drunk on the triumph of becoming a father. But Josephina walked into the baby's room and watched her. Suspicious, she waited for her baby to wake up. Did she come with a message from Pātti? From

Josephina's mother? It might only be possible to know in the first days of her life, when she still remembered being a part of everything.

Josephina accepted that taking a man's life would have consequences. But she thought they clung only to her. When she smelled the dead on her daughter's skin she felt sure something bad was coming. That she would look into her baby's eyes and see retribution looking back, but in the room there was only silence. There was only a little baby girl, born with a head of hair so full the midwife whooped when she crowned.

So Josephina let her sleep. Her ankles were groaning like they were uncertain about abruptly having less to carry. She walked back to her own bedroom, kissed Ravi, and he woke up smiling.

Glad you got to rest, she told him, hard day you must have had.

He laughed so loudly Josephina had to shush him. They lay side by side on their backs, basking in their success. Their bedroom had no curtains. In the haste of preparing the new house for the baby there wasn't time. They watched clouds drift over the moon.

Josephina's mind was already forgetting the pain of labour but her body shuddered with it. Ravi stroked the side of her thigh under the sheet. She felt lucky. The silences between them were as good as the conversations where Ravi made her laugh so hard she had to beg him to stop.

I thought of a name, said Ravi.

She still hadn't called their child anything but 'the baby'. Somehow, after the business of pregnancy and the drama of birth, Josephina had forgotten she wouldn't always be one.

Sithara, Ravi said. It means starlight.

On the dashboard of their car there is a plastic figurine of Buddha, fat and laughing. Beside him is a cream-coloured Virgin Mary. Small yellow wada mal at their feet tremble in the wind.

Today two-year-old Sithara is with her cousins, and Ravi and Josephina are driving to Wadduwa to pick up a table from the hotel they were married at. It is a small thing to travel so far for. Ravi packs ropes with hooks on the ends into the car and Josephina tucks a pillow behind her head so she can sleep while he drives. Their servant girl Anjali passes sweet hakuru appa wrapped in napkins through the passenger side window.

Although Ravi and his family are Catholic, he keeps a shrine to Ganesh in the house. When they pass Hindu temples he goes in and prays. On Fridays he often joins his colleagues at the mosque. It was Ravi's behaviour that threw Josephina's Catholicism into the light. She not only believed in one God, she feared him. Perhaps marriage, raising a family of her own, presenting as respectable, is a way to hide herself from him. Josephina is not sure if Ravi is curious, or superstitious and therefore deferential, but he touches the feet of each little figure lightly before starting the engine.

The night of their wedding, Ravi confessed he had never made love to a woman. They were alone in their hotel room, eating wedding cake on the balcony. Josephina still wore her white sari but Ravi was in swimming trunks. He shattered the cake into fine crumbs under his fork while he spoke. He was apologetic, as though she would scold him.

In return, and because it didn't seem like there would ever be another moment quite like this one, Josephina looked at the cake and told him about Mr Brooks. It was a light pressure on the back of her hand, an insistent tug at her shoulder, that stopped her from saying how the story really ended. Ravi didn't ask questions. The truth sat there, a stinger under her tongue, but she swallowed it.

He took her hand once she stopped talking, reaching naked arms across the table, and said that he was sorry. She nodded. In their marital bed for the first time, they did nothing but fall asleep, holding one another tight. That night all she wanted was to be close to someone who knew her and loved her still.

Wadduwa is supposedly an hour by car. It is closer to two with the traffic and Ravi's frequent stops for snacks.

Josephina is unsurprised when they end up giving a stranger, an uncle, a ride to Moronthuduwa.

When they arrive, Ravi slows down to point out the sights they both remember. A flaking billboard advertising shampoo, with a model whose lips are red like dried blood. Two and a half years later she still glares into the camera. The same man selling wooden elephants at a ferocious mark-up also sells his mother-in-law's chai. Josephina buys cups for herself and Ravi.

Ravi manoeuvres the car away from some coconut trees and they park by the back entrance to the hotel, at the service door. Josephina sits on the bonnet and feels the breeze coming off the ocean. He asks if she can smell the salt. She nods, closing her eyes. She feels him kissing her cheek, kissing the palms of her hands.

It's good to be back, she says. She holds the moment close, tasting the ocean, feeling the sand already glued to the bonnet of the car scratch at her calves. She thinks about their son floating, suspended, and touches her stomach.

I hope he's tall, at least, Ravi says, his eyes on the horizon.

Josephina snorts.

Fine. I hope he's ambitious. I want my boy to have a big life.

Ravi is still looking out. Past the sand, past the water, out to some unexplored part of the sky. She frowns; he never expressed any of this for Sithara. Josephina takes his hand, wanting to know why.

A bellboy whistles. He holds the sturdy wooden table they came for above his head and props the back door open with his foot. Ravi's youngest sister Nisha walks out of the hotel kitchen.

Nisha married a hotel owner six years ago, before Josephina became part of the family, and promptly took over the management of his largest hotel. She has thick gold bangles on her arms and the relaxed open smile of someone used to being in charge.

She insisted Ravi and Josephina be married in her hotel, for free. Josephina met Nisha's husband on the big day, and once more at Nisha's birthday a year later, but still she can't remember what his face looks like. Nisha burns so bright everyone around her is harder to see.

She runs to Josephina and turns her body to the side, laughing and shaking her head, Not even showing! How do you feel?

So much better than with my girl, Josephina says, kissing her sister-in-law on both cheeks.

Nangi, we can't stay. We have to go before the traffic gets bad again. Ravi doesn't stop to embrace his sister before strapping the table to the roof of the car. Josephina looks at him sharply but he avoids her gaze.

Nisha urges the bellboy back into the kitchen and he returns with lunch.

My brother might insist on being rude but he can't stop my sister from eating, can he? Nisha says.

Josephina takes the food and climbs back into the car, promising to return.

Why do you want this particular table so much anyway?

Ravi turns to Josephina, raising his eyebrows. Why do we want this *particular* table?

He drives away before she can scrabble together an answer.

In the years since they fell in love, got married and had Sithara, Ravi has talked about leaving Ceylon three times.

At the start it sounded so out of reach, like a daydream. Josephina was in her third trimester. Some days she washed her body four times because she couldn't bear the smell of herself.

Ravi said he had fantasies of taking them all to America, that they could live somewhere warm like Florida or California. They would go to baseball games and eat hot dogs and go on skiing holidays in the winter. His eyes shone at the prospect. No matter that none of them knew how to ski. Josephina thought when he said 'all' he meant the whole family and she asked how they could possibly get visas for fifteen of them.

The second and third times Ravi brought it up they had an argument. This daydream was starting to sound more like a plan that Josephina had never agreed to. Ravi said it was becoming easier to migrate to the UK as a doctor and asked Josephina what she thought about England.

She told him that she hated the English and their disgusting food. Ravi told her he didn't want to die in the same place he was born. There seemed to be a chasm between them Josephina hadn't noticed before.

Sithara was only a few months old then. Ravi put her to bed and tried again, more gently, to discuss it. Josephina sat down opposite, folded her arms and tried to look as though she hadn't already relinquished. Of course he wanted to emigrate. This desire for adventure was so much a part of Ravi's personality that she scolded herself for not having prepared for it.

If they stayed, he would be unhappy. Eventually he would resent her. No matter how many children she gave him, how noisy and bright their life was, how in love they continued to be, she would always be the person who stood in the way of Ravi taking the biggest bite he could out of life. So she gave in, with a caveat.

I want them to grow up here, I want them to be with their family. When Sithara is ten we will follow you anywhere that isn't England.

He swore that he would make them happy.

Ravi and Josephina arrive back in Colombo to pick up Sithara from Maude's. Maude smokes more than her brothers. She manages to be familiar without ever breaching personal space, something Josephina admires.

The two of them love to shop together, their children play together, they often mend clothes and sit side by side in the garden. When Josephina got pregnant for the second time, Maude placed a bottle of real champagne at the top of her bookcase like a shrine. For when you are free, she said.

Ravi carries Sithara past them to the car and Josephina kisses her on the forehead. Her cheeks are warm and her hair is like a cloud. She knows they should shave her baby hair off so it will grow back even and thick, but she simply cannot bring herself to touch it.

How was he with Nisha? Maude asks under her breath.

So rude! Josephina shakes her head at her husband's back.

They're too similar, Maude chuckles, both used to being the star of the show.

Children, Josephina says. She touches her stomach and prays her own will be friends.

Back home, they tuck Sithara into bed and eat their lunch for dinner. Nisha gave them a fine crab curry, a real treat. Josephina admires it before she eats; she will have to try her hand at a curry like this one. She feels grateful for her years with Inesh and Suji, where she could learn and taste and learn some more. Over the sink she squeezes lime on her fingers to get rid of the smell before washing her hands.

Ravi and Josephina untether their table from the car and place it in the middle of the living room, shushing each other and giggling. It reflects the light from long candles in real silver holders, a generous wedding present from Nisha.

Josephina sits with her legs in Ravi's lap while he rubs the soles of her feet.

You could have been nicer to your sister, she tells him.

He sighs, watching a tiny palli flit up the wall.

I know, he says. She just gets on my nerves.

The table is a small square. Fit for four people provided they are skinny. Suitable only for narrow chairs, purpose-built. But Ravi and Josephina didn't buy the chairs. To anyone else their excursion would seem entirely pointless.

Ravi raps his knuckles on the top and nods. He crouches below, shaking the legs of the table and grunting his approval. He picks it up and tries placing it in different corners of the room. It is awkward in all of them. Josephina laughs.

A little ugly. Very plain. Entirely impractical. He reaches his arms out for her, beaming.

And there, by flickering candlelight, they do what they did on the table three days after the night of their wedding. Transported to the last perfect morning of their honeymoon, while the evening whispers its agreement and their daughter sleeps soundly.

Sithara
1991, Hamilton

St John's Catholic Primary School is planted at the top of a hill. White weatherboard classrooms with dark blue roofs sit in a row, with a pretty church at the end. Just beyond the netball courts the ground falls away, disappearing into a sharp gully.

Children from the school and the neighbourhood hurtle down the slope. Sithara parks her car at the edge and starts to climb, bikes and scooters weaving around her. She cuts through, heading straight for the church.

Her work heels sink a little into the grass, and boys with small shoulders dip and lurch to avoid collision. They stare at her, this tense, suited woman, her hair with its own ecosystem. She feels no echoes of Suri at the sight of them, doesn't notice their chubby hands, the whirr of their feet, their determined pedalling. For so long now, her own memories have been a place she can't get back to.

Over weeks of covert phone conversations, Suri has laid out a plan. Sithara took his calls in her office, kicking her heels away under the desk.

First, the priest. Amma would want us to go to him. Then the next time Paul leaves without warning, I'll move in. We'll get the locks changed and put his things outside. Amma can take Annie to a hotel and stay with her until it is safe.

Suri said they will have to hide in Annie's room like fugitives and stake out the front door. This way they will be able to watch Paul coming up the driveway, finding his things packed and ready to go. Sithara tried to believe in the plan, that it could really play out the way her brother saw it. There are so many moving parts, and each time they have walked through it Sithara has detected another way it could fail. But Suri says it's now or never.

In the church office, Sithara stands to wait for the priest. Sitting makes her feel defenceless. She wears a grey skirt suit, a frown, and her twenty-five inches of shiny black hair, loose. It tickles the walls, the chair, trying to sweep up information. She doesn't like being alone in front of God.

The priest is twenty minutes late. Sithara pulls her earlobe. It has been a difficult week with Annie refusing to eat. She focused keen eyes on Sithara's nipple and then smacked it away from her mouth like a fly. Sithara tried endlessly. She sat with Annie in the rocking chair. She tried to feed while walking. She shoved her nipple in Annie's open mouth when Annie was laughing, but it was no use.

Every now and then she has the terrible feeling that Annie will grow up to be embarrassed by her. That she is too strange and too dark to have a nice Kiwi daughter, who will never have to take her accent off like a tight-fitting glove.

Father Gregory walks in still chewing. Sithara greets him and in his surprise he swallows too quickly. His eyes bulge and his hands grab at his neck. For a long silent moment, Sithara is concerned he will choke. She tries to smack him on the back but he shakes his head at her concern. He retreats behind his desk, forcing down his food. Sithara takes her cue to sit and the two of them stare at one another, awkward after such unexpected vulnerability.

Father Gregory slides bifocals onto his face and flicks through the letter Sithara wrote him. He has a straight nose and barely-there eyebrows. Tiny red veins spider across his cheeks. Sithara remembers coming to this country as a child and seeing a naked white body for the first time, being fascinated and a bit put off by it, the same way she can't look directly at yoghurt being stirred with a spoon.

So you want an annulment, Sitara? Father Gregory says, his voice stern.

It's Sithara, she says. He inclines his head and smiles, as though he knew the correct pronunciation but chose to ignore it.

No, I'm considering a divorce. I made that clear in my letter.

Have you *considered* an annulment?

She tries to wipe her face clean of disdain but her hair rustles with it.

My husband and I have a child. That seems – she struggles to find the words – unlikely.

Sithara has never been an enthusiastic member of Father Gregory's parish. Catholicism was one of Amma's conditions for moving to Hamilton. Annie will go to the parish school when she's old enough, and they make a point of attending church on Sunday.

Amma is at ease at church. She actually made friends. There are plenty of women her age volunteering, baking for one another, parading around their grandchildren. Amma quickly found a gang of Filipina aunties who welcomed her into their pew like a long-lost sister. Sithara uses feeding Annie as an excuse to head back to the car early.

You and your husband haven't been married long, it's as much of an option as divorce.

I don't think I'm comfortable with a piece of paper saying our marriage didn't exist, Father.

Father Gregory leans back in his chair and breathes out slowly. He steeples his fingers under his chin and assesses her over the line of his glasses.

Why do you want a divorce?

It's just not working.

It is quite unusual to separate when your first child is not even a year old, Mrs Fischer. Couples are usually busy with the bliss of being parents. He gestures at the air, to some imaginary nuclear family high on their own achievement. How does your mother feel about this?

The question rattles her.

Have you considered what this will mean for your daughter? Being raised as the child of divorce?

Suri has tried to tell Sithara that she is making this decision for Annie. She trusts him. They have weathered so much of this together. The things Sithara can't confess to Amma are impossible to hide from Suri.

You're planning to send Annie to the parish school?

Sithara nods.

Divorced parents are something we take into consideration when selecting our students, Father Gregory says.

The wedding had been a shambles. Sithara was four months pregnant. She and Paul fought the night before. She begged him not to go, she knew that her groom walking out the night before the wedding was a bad sign. But he left anyway. Libby bounded into her hotel room in the morning to find Sithara throwing up into the wastepaper basket, hair hiding the bruises on her neck.

He was right where he should be, in the end, waiting in the aisle when she walked up it. He saw her and gasped, got teary, exactly as grooms are supposed to. She wondered if Paul was the first person who had ever told her she was beautiful.

Then she remembered Appa and burst into tears. The priest officiating had looked around for someone to explain.

Has your husband been baptised into the Catholic faith? Father Gregory asks.

He was raised Presbyterian, she tells him.

Another excellent reason for annulment – interfaith marriages are easier to dissolve.

Two months later, when she was heavily pregnant and they were leaving the mall, Paul couldn't remember where he parked the car. Sithara knew she would be blamed for this, so she had darted back and forth trying to find it, steadying herself on the bumpers of all the cars that were not his. Paul grabbed her upper arm so tightly his nails left a mark. That night he kissed it and said how sorry he was. The purple indents really weren't big enough for anyone else to notice, but she stuck to long-sleeved shirts until they healed completely.

I don't imagine you're very interested in spending the rest of your life as a divorced woman. And why should you, when you could avoid it completely?

By getting an annulment instead of a divorce? she asks.

Exactly, says Father Gregory, nodding.

But if I was never married to my daughter's father, doesn't that make her a bastard?

Father Gregory grunts. He caresses her letter on the desk in front of him, looking pointedly at the clock behind Sithara's hair. She lets him squirm.

We don't use that word anymore, Mrs Fischer.

It's Ms Fernando. I never changed my name.

She picks up her briefcase and leaves.

When Annie was born she cried so hard it was like she came out with her heart already broken. Sithara was scared that she knew. That she had been listening to all the fighting and the crying and the pain.

She held her and apologised for bringing her into such a mess. She wanted to bundle Annie up, get on a bus and then a plane and never come back. To lull her to sleep, Sithara whispered stories about the two of them running away and living on a farm. They would have sheep and dogs and horses. They wouldn't need anyone else. She made the scene so vivid she came close to believing it.

The sun lit up the supermarket roses that Suri had brought to the maternity ward. Sithara had stayed in her daydream, wondering if the nurses would help her and her baby disappear. And then Paul came into the room carrying breakfast sandwiches and fluffing up her pillows and she ate gratefully and slept.

She was back at work just two weeks after giving birth. Paul still does casual hours as a painter. He says the money is better that way. He comes home at a different time every night, smelling of solvent.

It is Amma who takes care of Annie during the day. Sithara

expresses in the toilets between meetings with clients, but she still finishes work each night with heavy, aching breasts. Only last week, one of the partners pointed out that her nipples had soaked the front of her suit. She left to clean herself up, arms crossed tight over her chest.

In the beginning it was so easy to be with Paul. Sithara left her old routines behind. They spent more time together if she watched rugby on Saturdays with him and forewent her Sunday morning runs to snooze in his dusty bed. She would wake at midday to his hands stroking her hair.

And so much of the time it is still easy. Paul sang along to the radio just last night and smiled at her. She smiled back and felt so drawn to him she was worried her heart would catch fire and melt her whole body like wax.

Each time Sithara has considered leaving Paul, she has found a way not to. She realised he and Libby hated one another, so she learned to walk the space between the two of them like it was a tightrope. And that became normal.

A year later she found that Amma and Suri hated him too, but she had been sectioning her life so effectively she had barely noticed. This was a blow. It made her smaller, crushed under the weight of letting everyone around her down. She took Paul and left the rest behind.

And one day he rewarded her by proposing. She scrambled, she could feel the door closing. The way he looked at her when they met rose up out of the ground, real and bright and preserved entirely. She said yes. Then she got pregnant.

—

The firm Sithara works for overlooks the Waikato River. It is calm and ever-present, and she stares into it when she needs to feel something other than despair. She practises family law. All day she listens to women tell her about things their husbands and fathers have done to them. Most of the time Sithara wants to shut her door and curl up into a ball like a dog.

She doesn't always know where Paul ends and she begins. An argument will start. Sithara will know why and how it has started. She will be able to hold the catalyst in her hands: she laughed too loud; she was late picking him up; they ran out of some kind of food he was looking forward to. They will go back and forth, as couples do. Until he says something that throws her, like she is desperate for attention, or she is a whore.

Once she tried to lock herself in a room with Annie. She unearthed her fantasy of leaving, tried to conjure it as she had in the hospital. But her daughter just looked at her and started crying.

Paul sat outside and begged for forgiveness. He promised Sithara that he would make her bread and butter pudding the way she liked it, slightly undercooked and wobbly in the middle. He sounded so lonely, he needed her so badly. She thought about Annie's small brain absorbing his desperation, her fear.

Perhaps her marriage is simply the balance required for the gift of a baby like Annie. Who came out perfectly formed. Whose nails grow so fast Sithara has to trim them while Annie sleeps, peeling shards off the blanket and dropping them into a plastic cup.

Sithara can read Paul's moods. She knows the light in his eyes can turn sharp as flint. She can smell when a storm is coming. She tastes the electricity in the air like burnt toast.

In the foyer the receptionist tells her there is a man waiting. Sithara considers walking out again. Instead she nods a thank you and takes the stairs.

At her office she is surprised to find her secretary Emma and Suri, waiting with a bottle of champagne.

Annah! You've got skinnier. She hugs him tight. And balder.

He laughs and unwraps the foil around the bottle.

What are we celebrating? Emma asks.

Emma is good at her job. She's in her fifties. She cares about clients without being nosy. She has a slight lisp and she brings thick slices of ginger crunch to work every Friday. She also seems to dislike Paul, although Sithara is sure he's never given her a reason.

We're celebrating me, Suri says, his champagne glittering. I'm moving to Hamilton to live with my sister, our mother who hates me, and my sweet little niece.

He gives Sithara one of his proudest smiles and she feels her legs might buckle.

Emma, would you mind checking with the partners about what we have to submit on Monday?

Emma shuts the door behind her.

Sithara looks out the window to remind herself of the river sludging away. Still there. The carefully tended trees along the roadside. Still there. Her hair wafts across her eyes, blocking her vision, and she has to use two hands to push it away.

I'm not leaving him, Annah.

Silence. The sound of the walls cracking.

Not now? Or not ever?

Sithara shrugs. She spits hair out of her mouth. She tugs at a huge strand that has threaded itself between her teeth.

I'm not bringing up Annie alone. You remember what it was like, after we lost Appa.

Suri's eyes flash. For a brief second he looks like Amma.

That man is *nothing* like Appa. The words shoot out like light.

I know. But I love him.

Suri's shoulders drop, his fury evaporating. He has never worn anger well. He sinks into her office couch and looks up at her like he might cry.

It's your life, Akki, he says. You're throwing away your life.

He has always been Sithara's best friend. She thinks of how much the two of them have survived and feels certain he is the only person in the world who has ever known everything about her.

You need to get angry. You need to be angry at him. You didn't even get a chance to rest after you had Annie. That's *his* fault. I hardly see you anymore and I know that's his fault. And what about the beatings? Do you think they're just going to stop? He's not going to stop until you're dead. Suri has tears flowing down his cheeks but his voice is small, like the past already disappearing.

You can't stay, he says, standing. If you don't leave, I will.

They look at each other, Sithara refusing to cry, Suri weeping.

He's my family, Suri.

So what am I?

She becomes aware she is a coward, that perhaps she has always been. But self-knowledge just makes this inevitable, already done. Her hair stretches out. Her roots are on fire, each strand staging a revolt. Sithara revolts back.

You're nothing.

Annie
2018, London

Twenty-one years later most of the details are hazy, but Annie tries anyway to explain what her childhood with Paul was like. It's there, but she has to dig for it, rummage around in her past, scrape her fingertips on the thought of him.

She talks about Paul coming home from work and lifting her up onto his shoulders. She also talks about being so scared to leave her bedroom that she would pee in cups and throw the pee out the window. The silences that choked them all. How his mood dictated everyone else's. Falling asleep and waking up somewhere different. Her mum would carry her out of the house and bundle her into Gran's spare bedroom. Gran would greet her in the morning as though nothing at all had happened in the night.

She tells Suri about leaving for school with Gran and looking at the windows of her house and seeing all the curtains pulled tight. About how she had to give evidence in court. She was placed behind a screen. The prosecutor looked like Miss Honey from *Matilda*.

She remembers the shame. Listening to the defence describing Paul kicking her mum in the stomach, the embarrassment of not being able to stop him, the grief of not calling the police sooner.

Suri slumps on the couch, the bright afternoon sun unforgiving, his head limp. Every now and then he wipes the back of his hand over his mouth and nods as though confirming something to himself.

Annie keeps going. She talks about how her mum's body sounded hollow. Her hands are shaking. She doesn't want to talk about what happened afterwards but now she can't stop.

She tells Suri how she ran at Paul when her mum's body stopped moving, how she grabbed his ears and twisted, screamed right into his eardrums. How she forced her fingers inside his mouth and peeled his cheeks away from his gums like the thick skin of an onion.

This is when it ended – with Paul turning on her and advancing like he wanted to kill her, his body blocking out all the light there had ever been. With Annie running away and falling on the stairs. It ended with Gran picking her up.

He got three years. Annie found out later that the judge was scared of the long-term effects on her mental health. She'd had to show them her bald spot, the bruises on her wrists from her own teeth.

The time afterwards, too, was strange. Counsellors, her primary school teacher, friends of Gran's from church, all of them must have known a little of what happened because they tried to talk to her about it. They struggled to make it to the end of their sentences. Wrung their hands. Annie gave them nothing, just stared, watched them twitch while they promised her that things happen for a reason, that she and her mum would be stronger because of what they had been through.

Even then she knew this was a lie. Her scars weren't trophies – they were ugly and useless and they remained in Annie's body even when the skin over the top of them healed.

Suri and Annie sit among the wreckage. Empty cups from endless pots of tea. The butter in its dish, soft and dipped in the middle. The blankets they have wrapped themselves in to listen to one another talk cast off as punctuation, strewn across the floor.

Annie feels peaceful. Perhaps the jet lag made her bold. Or maybe she's just light because she emptied herself. Annie has never handed so much of her life to someone else.

Suri gets up and goes to the fridge. He fills a glass with ice and then water and drinks it in one go. Then he presses his palms against his forehead and stands in the middle of the kitchen, silent.

Annie laughs at him. You've got brain freeze, haven't you?

Suri shakes his head but doesn't move. She waits, wondering if he is annoyed at her. He has tidy feet, like someone who gets regular pedicures. Gran sits every night and moisturises her feet before getting into bed. Her elbows too. She twists her wrists in small circles and sings to herself.

Suri pulls his hands away and Annie sees his face is streaked with tears. She stands on impulse, wanting to comfort him.

How long was it? How long was he around?

Until I was seven. He came back into the picture when I was sixteen – they must have been talking for a while before that, I don't know. The second time they broke up, I was eighteen and long gone.

I'm so sorry, Annie, he says.

She doesn't want an apology. She wants to go back to eating, to telling stories. She wants to change the subject entirely and speak to him of joyful things.

It doesn't matter anymore, Annie says. She desperately wants to know about Suri's husband. What the two of them do for work. How they built such a beautiful life. Why he has stayed inside for days just listening to her. What else he remembers about the grandad she never got to meet. She wants to talk to him about Gran's cooking. She wants to know what meals he used to ask for on his birthday.

She waits for him to sit down again, but he doesn't move.

I wish you knew what it was like for me with her, with both of them, he says, voice quivering.

It's done now, Suri, she says.

Suri thumps his chest. Hard at first and then softer, until he is only clutching at his heart.

I feel like I'm studying them, she confesses. White men. All of them. Like I'm trying to see if there's anything inside.

Suri is silent.

Any care, any love, she continues. I never found any. Or if I did, I didn't believe it.

She is hoping for recognition, hoping to meet Suri on common ground. But he stays still, head bowed, pressing his palms to his forehead, like he is trying to protect himself from the past that flies low around his head, circling again and again.

Josephina

Sigiriya rises up out of dusty trees. Stone pavilions criss-cross the fields leading up to it. From this distance it seems flat, the image on the front of a postcard. Josephina looks at her children – Sithara waiting to be impressed, Suri oblivious. He and their servant boy Chintu squat on the ground playing with their wretched marbles. Thick lines of colour dripping down the rock call out to Josephina. She's running out of time to say goodbye.

Like every other monument here, Sigiriya has its own guards. Their guns are large but treated like clothing, slung over a shoulder, dangling from a waist. All guns fill Josephina with dread. Even when unused, it is impossible to forget their purpose. It feels like looking at something one shouldn't, the private made public.

Ravi insisted on a holiday. He wanted the children to have sweetened memories of Sri Lanka before he wrested them away. Josephina tried to get them to go without her. She wanted to kick her feet up at Maude's and have a cigarette. There was even talk of Nisha coming up for the day.

Instead, they left Colombo on this farewell tour before leaving in a month, for good. Ravi has tried to make the move sound like an adventure, promising the children that going on a plane will be the most marvellous experience of their lives, that their new country is better than the only home they have ever known. New Zealand, where there are no guns but the winters are freezing cold.

Josephina knows she needs to make peace with it. This is what she agreed to, no more or less. But every day she resists optimism, resting instead in her own misery.

Breaking the news to the children went better than either of them expected. Sithara was too preoccupied by a Hindi film to pay attention. Suri was half-asleep, his head resting on Sithara's shoulder. She had to give him custard to wake him up. He made her push the spoonfuls into his mouth like a baby, giggling, custard dripping down his chin. Sithara's eyes hovered just above Ravi's shoulders, trying to watch the television.

What about 'Old Zealand'? Suri asked.

Josephina replied, There's no such thing.

Well actually, there is a Zeeland, Ravi said. It's part of the Netherlands. This surprised them all. Suri blinked, then burst into laughter.

Josephina cupped his cheeks in her hand and gave thanks for her children's ignorance. They have never had to survey their parents for signs of deception. All she wants is for both of them to remain children as long as possible.

Chintu, though, understood what it meant. When they told him, he dropped the bowl he was carrying in shock. Josephina saw his face twist in rage before he bent to pick it up. When he stood again the anger was gone.

Two weeks later, the Fernando family bought backpacks and suitcases. The night before they left for Dambulla, Josephina stayed late at Maude's. She helped her put the twins to bed, then sat at the dining table mending Suri's old trousers. They prolonged the inevitable by talking of everything else. Josephina felt heavy with sadness, aware that every moment was the last.

The children, too, are close to their extended family. Sithara often arrives home to cousins and aunts. To four fat hands at the gate: Maude's twins Vida and Vidhesh. Josephina spends her afternoons in the kitchen making dinner, Maude helping, Nisha pretending to, their conversation rising into the roof and scaring the sparrows, feathers flying every time they laugh.

Chintu grates coconut in the back room, singing softly in Tamil, with Suri crouched, barefoot, on the ground beside him, playing marbles or helping sweep the floor. Ravi can be found in the garden, his papers a mess, calling for Josephina and then pulling her onto his lap despite her protests that the chapati will burn, cheering like a soccer fan when he sees Sithara. This is the tune of their daily routine.

Karnan and Edward come with their families for dinner. Edward left his job at the museum, not long after Josephina and Ravi were married, to join Karnan's business.

Karnan is brash. He ignores his nieces and nephews and often his own wife. He gave Josephina a strange look when he met her. Edward married a sweet girl they all call Chootie. She walks with a limp and has a perfectly oval face, like an Estee Lauder model.

For her own peace of mind, Josephina is careful to never be alone with Edward. Though he isn't over-familiar, it's the way he listens to her, with his head cocked to the side, the way his eyes caress her hands, the way his gaze finds hers first when he enters a room, that tells her to keep her distance.

Josephina suspects Ravi feels a certain satisfaction about it all. She overheard them in the garden, Sithara asking why Edward Uncle was always so morose. She heard Ravi's tone when he told her that Chootie was not Edward's first love, that the woman he truly wanted ended up with someone else. His soft triumph.

Sometimes her brothers-in-law stay until morning. They drink arrack for hours in the garden, their arguments cascading with the drink. Josephina usually persists with going to bed at a decent time, only to be woken by Ravi's wild giggle. She leaves her bedroom and wraps a cardigan over her nightgown, stealing a cigarette from whoever is in the middle of one.

Ravi has decided things are getting worse in Sri Lanka. Karnan disagrees. The two of them often end up shouting. Ravi finds Karnan's trust in their government embarrassing. Josephina suspects Karnan would like her a little more if she weren't Tamil. But all of them join in on complaining about the British.

✦

Josephina wraps her waist-length hair around itself in a thick bun and slips hairpins out of her mouth. Ravi is several metres in front, speaking with a family that have just come down the rock, their faces shining with sweat.

Fat little Suri struts towards Sigiriya, tilting his head as he walks to see the entire thing. His small body slants dramatically in the process. Ravi laughs aloud. Josephina spent the whole car ride constructing a makeshift chain for Suri's spectacles out of string and rubber bands, worried he would peer over the side and lose the only thing saving him from blindness. Somehow, the carefully homemade chain makes him look unloved.

Chintu keeps running forward to whisper in Suri's ear. He doesn't speak Sinhala and Suri only knows a small amount of Tamil, so the two of them have built a language all their own. Chintu isn't much older than Suri himself, probably nine or ten. He says he doesn't know and the family has no way to tell for sure. Josephina suspects he might be closer to twelve – his upper lip has started to fuzz and he is beginning to smell more like a man than a boy.

A year ago he had shown up at their front door asking for a job. He had shards of soap and a change of clothes in a brown paper bag, miserable rags wrapped around the soles of his feet to serve as shoes. He pointed to the bird feeder, claiming he could fix it. None of them had even noticed it was broken. He was so malnourished he looked like a corpse.

They didn't really need the help. Josephina quit teaching for good after she had Suri and both her children were old enough that doing some housework while taking care of them was manageable. She had a strange feeling about Chintu. She didn't like the way he spoke to her in Tamil first, exposing their shared difference. She assured him they spoke only English in this house and he murmured, *Okay Mummy* and smiled.

Sithara and Suri hid behind Ravi and listened, staring, as he talked Chintu through the terms of his employment, where he would sleep and what days he would have off.

Chintu has perfected the art of being visible only when he wants to be. He has twisted muscles from a childhood of labour and eyes that glow like orbs. They seem suspended sometimes of their own accord, floating in the corner of the room. His front teeth are chipped and there are triangle-shaped burn marks across his back like a mosaic. Some are dark patches, but others are raised as though the skin bubbled and froze.

Only a few months after he arrived, Ravi found Suri and Chintu sleeping in Suri's bed. He was leaving for the hospital early and went in to say good morning. He wandered back to the bedroom, waking Josephina to ask if she thought it was odd.

She assured him that it was not, smiled and waved goodbye. But her feet led her to her son's room. They were curled like kittens under the sheet. Chintu's hands were balled into fists and Suri's were clasped around them, like he was absolving Chintu of something.

Although early, the temperature is starting to climb. The sky is still the clean blue of dawn. It makes Sigiriya gleam. Sithara starts to wipe her hair out of her face and then smells the tea-tree that Josephina has covered her arms in and groans.

You'll thank me later, girl, Josephina tells her.

Sithara tosses her head to throw her hair off her neck. It settles obediently, ending like a veil in the small of her back.

Hardly anyone here is dressed for exercise. The men are wearing jeans and good shirts. They amble slowly, talking and laughing, stopping often to smoke. Josephina dressed her children like tourists—in sportswear and sneakers. Ravi shook his head when he saw them, but Josephina figured it was better to be practical.

She herself wears navy pants, a white shirt cropped short

to her waist, silk scarf around her neck and a small satchel tucked into the pocket of her shirt containing her cigarettes.

Josephina considers how she has changed. It is true that she takes pride in stepping out beside her handsome husband and their bright-eyed children. She likes how it feels to be part of a place, enjoys being someone who is known and respected. Perhaps she covets the wrong things, has turned into the kind of woman she would have once sneered at when she was holed up in the back room of the parlour with the girls.

Ravi walks with his hands in his pockets, quizzing Sithara and Suri. Why did King Kashyapa build his fortress?

To keep his naughty brother out, Suri says.

Correct. He built his kingdom high so he could watch the land around him closely.

He loves to tell them stories.

Many, many centuries ago, Kashyapa, the bastard first son of King Dhatusena, seized the throne from his father in a bloody coup. The legitimate heir to the throne, his younger brother Moggallana, fled to India. Ravi points to Suri and Sithara as he speaks, trying to cast Suri as the good guy and Sithara as the bad one. Sithara refuses his attempts to pull her into the game, rolling her eyes.

Kashyapa, Ravi continues, who knew that his days as King were numbered, built what he believed to be an impenetrable fortress on top of the rock, ordering labourers to carve the boulders at the bottom into lion's claws. But of course, after years building and training a loyal army in India, Moggallana returned to his homeland and seized the throne from his brother in battle. Kashyapa died by his own sword rather than face defeat.

Even Chintu has his full-moon eyes glued to Ravi's face. Suri skewers invisible soldiers, cheering for himself and his victory. When Ravi finishes, Sithara tells him she doesn't like stories with no girls in them. Josephina chuckles at Ravi's disappointment. At the steps they shift into single file.

It really is a sight. The lion's feet are taller than two men and wide with vicious claws. From here they can look up and see one entire side, a staircase zigzagging back and forth, lines of people moving slowly both ways. Suri is already begging to go last, forcing Chintu to drag him by the hand.

As they climb, Josephina considers how little she has seen of her adoptive country. She has not been up into the mountains, nor travelled through the forests. Where was the time? Who could spare the money when there are children to dress and a new life to save for? But now that she is rising to the top of this sacred place, seeing her family in awe, she has some regrets.

Annah, if you're at the front it will take us all day, Sithara says, and pokes her brother's soft back. Chintu turns over his shoulder to give her a frown, as though telling her off.

Chintu is still a mystery. They don't know why he has

no family or where the burns come from. He must have been very young when he got them. When Chintu works outside, he does so with no shirt and Josephina watches, hypnotised by his scars. They are fat, like bruised caterpillars.

She can't empathise with him. Although her childhood had its own terrors, she was able at least to go to school, to sleep in her own room every night. But it seems possible that this boy who showed up at their door, in pieces, is the only person in Josephina's house who could really understand her.

They rise up out of the humidity into the clouds. The air is cool here.

Amma, what kind of food will they have at the new school? Sithara asks.

Josephina shakes a cigarette out of the silver case in her pocket and faces the rock to light it. A lot of potatoes I suspect, she says, blowing the smoke out slowly.

Karnan Uncle told me there are sheep in New Zealand, Sithara says. Millions of sheep.

Josephina nods. Sithara shakes her head and sighs as though she simply cannot comprehend what one country would do with so many sheep. Josephina presses a thumb to Sithara's forehead, relaxing her brow.

Where we are going, she assures her, there will not be so many sheep.

Yesterday, before they left for Dambulla, Josephina found Sithara in her bedroom. She was looking down at her bare feet, lifting her toes on one foot then the other, feeling the cool concrete on her soles.

No matter how hot it was outside, how low the leaves hung, how lank or exhausted Josephina felt in the midday hours before the rain broke and the city relaxed, the floors in her house were always cool.

It is not Sithara she worries about as much as Suri, though she struggles to define why. Suri and Chintu sleep together most nights now. They pulled closer after Suri worked out Chintu would not be joining them in New Zealand. She hears Suri's door whisper open before she falls asleep.

✦

At the top, new conquerors of their own strange city, Ravi turns to her, smug as anything.

The landscape unfurls at her feet like a carpet. This king must have felt like he ruled the universe. Josephina is struck by the thought that she has only seen the world's underbelly.

Yes, I'm glad I came, she says to Ravi.

Sithara, Suri and Chintu run past, through the tourists and out of sight. Ravi kisses her hand. I'll go, he says.

The air is clear, the mountains stare straight back at her. She walks the sunburnt earth nodding at the families she passes. This could be the pinnacle of her own life. Surely she has had more joy in the last decade than any one person deserves.

Two brothers, their narrow chins pitted and marked, pose for a photo. A baby slaps an open hand on the dirt at her mother's feet and laughs at the dust that spirals up in response. The sun warms Josephina's bones.

Ravi would tell her she is being a pessimist. They don't know what awaits them in New Zealand so why assume the worst? Of course he is right. But Josephina is not sure she can change her nature so easily.

Amma! Nothing has ever looked this big.

She finds her family. Suri is perched on a little wall, gawking at the scenery. The summit is crowded with small constructions. Empty doorframes, rows of bricks that are only one or two high, low walls that used to be the edge of something grander.

There is a dip in the ground ahead like a chair. Ravi offers to take a photo for an American couple who have a huge black camera, and the man lowers himself into it, releasing his camera like he is handing over his child, unable to wipe the concern off his face.

From the ground, it seems as though the top of Sigiriya is a flat plane, but in fact it is a multi-level network of courtyards and pools dug up out of the stone. Ravi tells the children the pools were once functional; they used to fill up with water and feed a complicated irrigation system. Sithara wanders away from him, puts her hands around her face to block out the sun and stares up at the sky. Chintu tugs Suri and the two of them climb the tiny walls and jump off. All of them seem freer here, made different by this place.

On the way down, Sithara stops at the frescoes and stares. Women decorate the walls. Their breasts are full and stick straight out of their chest, the line from breast to waist is concave, their hips wide. Josephina stands next to her, trying to see the paintings through her daughter's eyes.

I don't know if it is good or bad, Ammi.

If what is good or bad?

That girls were the thing they wanted most to look at.

Josephina pulls away from the paintings to assess her daughter. When did she start to think about these things? And how is Josephina supposed to help her come to terms with them?

Do you want to do some exploring by yourself before we go?

Sithara nods, still staring at the artwork. Josephina unhooks her watch and straps it around Sithara's wrist, telling her to keep an eye on Suri and be back at the car in half an hour.

Water buffaloes bask in a trench of shallow, milky water. Their ears flap away the mosquitoes, their eyelashes are long and fluffy. White herons decorate the grass.

Josephina takes Ravi's hand and they walk back over fields growing thick with tourists. They made it up and down again before the rush.

The sun is firmly in the sky now, strong and unrelenting.

Shall we go somewhere to eat before we get back to the hotel? she asks Ravi.

Yes, I want kottu.

Josephina nods her assent. She likes holiday Ravi. He could do with working less.

Though they take their time wandering through the grounds and sunning themselves, when they arrive at the car the children are not there. Josephina sits in the passenger seat, trying to dispel her concern with a cigarette, while Ravi lies across the backseat, dozing.

Sigiriya watches both of them, not so big now that they have scaled it in one short morning.

Don't fret, they'll be here soon, Ravi tells her.

Josephina lurches forward, sticks her head out the window. Ravi's voice, usually strong and soothing, fades to static. The people around have all turned and are walking fast towards an incident out of sight.

Josephina throws her cigarette to the ground and follows them without waiting for Ravi, dread mounting with her steps. She hears Sithara's voice before she sees her. Her daughter is shouting, pleading with a woman the same age as Josephina.

I need to find my amma, my amma please.

The aunty talking with her does not look sympathetic.

Josephina sidesteps her and crouches down in front of Sithara, gripping her shoulders. What happened? Are you okay? Where's your brother?

Ammi, it was so horrible. Sithara hugs her tight.

Josephina checks her for bruises. What was horrible? Who hurt you? Tell me right now.

No, not me. In the bathroom, Suri and Chintu. I feel sick.

Josephina's heart slows, almost stops. She holds Sithara by her chin. What are you saying?

Sithara puts her hands over her eyes. She whispers, I went to the boy's bathroom to look for Suri. Everything was dark but I saw what they were doing.

Suri sprints towards them, darting through the people, yelling, She's wrong! Akki is lying. He wheels around to face Sithara, launches at her like he is about to hit her. Ravi appears and hauls him off.

Josephina stares straight at Chintu, emerging from the bathrooms with his head held high. Her eyes scald him, rip a layer of skin off his body.

She lifts the boy up by his collar, so that he can see right into her eyes. He flinches and begins to tremble.

Josephina tells him slowly that she will kill him. She tells him nobody will mourn the loss of his life because he has no one. He has no one apart from Josephina and her family and now he has lost them forever so who is left to mourn? She throws him to the floor and he lands on skinny knees with a crack.

In her mind Josephina can see Chintu haunting the dark toilet stall. She can see him forcing Suri to do disgusting things, wounding her son in a way from which he will never recover. She wants to tear his penis from his body and hear the skin break.

Suri is pulling at her leg, weeping. Sithara rushes to Chintu to help him but Josephina drags her off and slaps her, hard. She drops to the ground and sits with her legs out in front, holding her face.

You were supposed to look after your brother.

Her daughter looks up in disbelief. Her mother has never laid a hand on her before. She whimpers for her appa, but Ravi is asking Suri if he is okay, over and over again.

Josephina looks at her son. How can she bear to call herself a mother after allowing him to suffer like this?

Heavy footsteps crunch the ground. Two soldiers, striding from the ticket office with their guns. Josephina realises the crowd around them has grown. Chintu prostrates himself at Josephina's feet. Sithara starts crying. She sounds small, and far away. All of them do.

One soldier leans over to steady Josephina's shaking hands and light her cigarette. He asks Ravi what the problem is, but Ravi just shakes his head.

The children were playing a game, he says.

The soldier's greedy eyes hang on Josephina's mouth. A man's voice breaks through the crowd. He is being directed away by the other soldier but he turns to call back, Leviticus 20:13!

What is he talking about, my dear? the soldier says, lifting the crucifix on Josephina's neck with the edge of his finger. Ravi moves closer.

Chintu is still on the ground. The other soldier assesses him like prey, shoves him with the butt of his rifle. Suri rushes over but Ravi grabs his collar.

He's with us, Ravi says.

The soldiers nod. The one who lit Josephina's cigarette cocks his head to the side and smiles. He nudges Chintu with the toe of his boot. Chintu looks up and his eyes find Suri's. Josephina watches in horror as the two of them reach for one another, their small hands just kissing.

I caught him stealing, Josephina says. Ravi shakes his head sadly but stays silent.

The Fernando family watch as the soldiers pull Chintu away. Suri is sobbing. Sithara is clenching and unclenching her fists. Ravi follows Chintu's small head as it bobs out of view, the light in his eyes dying. Josephina takes deep drags on her cigarette, hand on hip. Her teeth chatter, rattle around in her head. Suri jumps when she tries to touch him. Sithara can't even meet her eyes.

The drive back to Dambulla is silent. Josephina feels her life slipping out of her grasp.

Sithara

2000, Hamilton

The prison is half an hour out of Hamilton, surrounded by lush fields and livestock. The building itself is grim, chalky, with a barbed wire fence, and it stands at a fork in the road. A young oak tree springs up from a circle of grass in the concrete courtyard at the entrance.

The prison and the landscape around it are so at odds that Sithara wonders if it is intentional. Would it be better to look out at something beautiful, remind yourself of what was waiting for you? Or would such expansiveness just beyond the walls only recall what you were missing?

She imagines future developers buying the land as Hamilton's population grows beyond its borders, turning it into a satellite village. Would they have to be transparent about who used to be housed here? Would it make a difference? White people never seem to care what it is they build their lives on top of.

Today is the day Paul gets out.

Sithara had woken at 3 am in a cold sweat. She had drunk glass after glass of water in the bathroom. The sound of her teeth hitting the glass, the splash of water dribbling onto bare feet had brought her back to the world. Her hair kept bouncing out of the bun she had tried to tie it into.

She had dressed herself as though it were any other Friday. It wasn't. It was also Amma's fifty-ninth birthday. Tonight, before she meets Libby, Sithara will stop at a yum cha restaurant to pick up Amma's favourite dessert – mango pudding, which they will eat with cans of evaporated milk.

Sithara had to pay the restaurant double to get them to make it on a Friday night. She used to get Amma cake, but two years ago the three of them – Sithara, Amma and Annie – ceremoniously took a vote and decided not to restrict themselves to a singular, socially acceptable birthday treat.

Annie gets chocolate eclairs on her birthday. Sithara buys a whole tray, piles them on top of one another and skewers them with candles. For Sithara's birthday, Amma makes watalappan, coconut custard. Spiced and smooth and caramel. Sithara thinks of Appa when she eats it.

She made Annie run over to Amma's before they left for school with a bunch of daffodils and some hand cream. Annie waved from the car as they left and told her to remember to record *Pokémon*.

When Sithara got to work, she walked straight to the office of a partner named Brendan and asked to borrow his car. A black Holden Commodore with tinted windows. She likes Brendan. He's friendly and less racist than the others. Brendan didn't ask why Sithara needed his car, or why she came to work that morning just to get it and leave again.

She parks the car close enough to the entrance to see the men coming and going, but not close enough to see the expression on their faces. She doesn't know what time Paul will be released. She doesn't know who is coming to get him. All Sithara knows is that today is the day her ex-husband will rejoin the world.

She eats salted pretzels and tries to read over her cases to fill the time. She thinks about what liquor stores she will pass on the way home and whether two bottles of wine will be enough to say thank you to Brendan. She wonders why even simple favours from men make her feel ill at ease. She hopes Annie will grow up without this tendency to defer to the men around her.

The security guard wanders over to her car just before one.

She winds down the window and, smiling, says, Good afternoon.

Afternoon, love.

He is white. He looks about fifty. He has deep red acne scars along his cheeks like fault lines.

I'm a family lawyer at Granger, Mark and Smith, she says handing over her business card.

She has a story ready to go, but he waves away Sithara's card and leans his back on the car. His torso is at the height of her mouth. He smells of sweat and piccalilli.

He sighs. It's hard for the wives, he says. Even arseholes manage to find women who love them.

Her stomach churns. She points to the oak tree. That brightens the place up, doesn't it?

The security guard nods and leans in closer.

Last autumn that tree dropped all its leaves overnight. I've never seen anything like it. I don't know if there was a storm or what, but when I got to work that day you couldn't see the concrete for the leaves.

He smiles and raps the top of the car with his knuckles like he is sending her off, and walks away. Sithara winds the window back up and seals herself inside, sliding along the seat until her eyes sit just above the line of the darkened window.

It's not until two o'clock that anything happens. Sithara is thinking about Annie, about how Annie's therapy is going and whether it would be appropriate to ask the therapist if her child is really okay, when the doors to the prison open, and just like that, her ex-husband walks out.

Sithara grasps the handle of the car door, fighting with herself. Paul is thin like a toothbrush. It makes him look even taller. His hair bristles out at weird angles and he holds a plastic bag with what looks like books inside it. He is wearing the same pants he wore the day the police took him away – grey trackpants he used to sleep in – and new-looking sneakers.

She wants to cradle him in her arms. She wants to buy him clothes and take him to dinner and tell him again and again that she is sorry she left him to rot. She wants to ask him what prison is really like, take the full hit of his answers without looking away.

Sithara hasn't dated or slept with anyone since Paul was convicted. For the first two years this seemed like a standard result of trauma, a natural response. But recently some of her colleagues have been offering to set her up, encouraging her to put herself *out there*. She checks her face in the mirror and unlocks the car door.

A bus pulls up and stops close to Paul. Sithara watches his shoulders rise and drop again, like he is sighing with relief. Sithara stares directly at him, willing him to notice her. She can't clearly see Paul's face, can't tell if there is relief in his eyes.

He starts moving towards the bus and she knows she has about thirty seconds to get out of Brendan's car and go to him. To slough away all the time that has passed with an apology and a kiss.

She stays in the car, in the dark, hiding from her worst self. She has no idea if he feels her close, but to Sithara it's like there is a rubber band around them. She hears it twanging.

Before the bus starts up she drives away, crumpling the business card she is still holding into a ball.

✦

Sithara only comes to this bar when Libby Zhu is in town. She's the special occasion. At work, Sithara is consumed by the lives of other people. She has a digital clock on her desk with an alarm so she doesn't work through the night. Every evening when it goes off, it feels like a bolt of sunlight. She drives home anticipating stories of Annie's day at school, eating Amma's food.

This evening she is alone in the just-opened bar, sitting with her shoulders hunched and curving inward like a question mark. She likes being on her own here, in cafes too, even movie theatres. There is a reverence to empty bars. The high-ceilinged room reminds her of church.

Sithara made partner two years ago. She handles the same kind of cases she always has. Most of her clients are mothers, some are foreign. It's not that they always get on because of it — in fact, sometimes it can make things harder. Her few South Asian clients have all seemed embarrassed by her status as a divorced single mother, like it tarnishes them too.

The bartender returns with a case of wine. Sorry for making you wait, she says.

She's new. She sounds Iranian, maybe. Amma would be

able to tell. She has heavy brows and delicate corkscrew curls dyed a fake ginger. There is a green jewelled stud in her nose, a speck of what looks like mascara fallen just above it. She stands in shadow, but her skin and her eyelids glow and the evening light collects around her with purpose, as though presenting her. She is like Amma – someone whose beauty undoes the world she moves through.

What can I get you? she asks.

A gin and tonic please, Sithara says. Actually, two. One for my friend.

The bartender puts the case down and leans back, taking in Sithara's tailored waistcoat and matching suit pants.

Where are you from? she asks.

Invercargill, Sithara says instinctively. Well, Sri Lanka. You?

I'm Mojdeh, she says, refusing to answer her own question. She is looking at Sithara's hair with an expression close to unease. Her fingers whirr back and forth across the handle of the ice scoop. Sithara pulls at the collar of her shirt and casts her eyes around the room.

Blessedly, Libby thunders through the door. She squeals when she sees Sithara, and starts talking about how long the drive from Auckland was. She's this happy every time. Despite the day she's had, seeing Libby makes Sithara feel warmer.

Her oldest friend winding up an English and History teacher had seemed to Sithara like a kind of failure, at first. But Libby loves it. It took Sithara time to realise that not everyone uses their career as a way to prove something to others.

Libby hasn't put on weight exactly, but she has thickened; it is like her bones have expanded. Her arms and wrists are wider. She is still uncomfortable in her new body, like she is trying to shrug it off.

The love Sithara has for Libby isn't arrow-straight. It is bound up in competition. She assesses Libby when she sees her, holds their lives side by side without really even meaning to. She checks what one of them has against what the other doesn't.

Libby has a loving but unattractive husband. Sithara has a well-paid but thankless job. Libby had five miscarriages and stopped trying. Sithara has a nine-year-old. They both look young for their age. Libby is engaging. Sithara is intimidating.

Libby clinks her glass on Sithara's and starts drinking before she sits down.

Thank you, she tells Mojdeh, who is slicing lemons.

Wow, you're pretty.

Mojdeh nods and keeps slicing.

They talk about their lives. Sithara brags about Annie's gymnastics and Libby talks about her students. She recently moved her Dad up to Auckland to live with her and her husband, and says she is cooking Chinese food for the first time in her adult life.

I couldn't bear to make dumplings at home. I wouldn't

even let Josh pick Chinese restaurants when we went out to eat. But then Mum died and everything changed.

They watch the bar fill up around them. Sithara didn't realise, until she started coming here to meet Libby, that this is where men go. Sometimes there are a few women. But most of the time it is only men, sitting in groups of three or four, growing more excitable as the night goes on. They always seem to be just warming up when she and Libby leave. Sithara wonders what it must feel like to be so free.

She raises her eyebrows at Mojdeh, signalling for a second round of drinks.

I don't know why I spent so much of my life hating all of that, you know? Libby chews her straw. Did you? she adds, noting Sithara's lack of enthusiasm.

It was different for me, Sithara says. Maybe because I wasn't born here. I don't know. I don't feel like I ever really had a choice.

You both sound like them. Like *Kiwis*, Mojdeh says, implacable, handing over their drinks. How do you know each other?

We were Asian in Invercargill, Sithara says.

In the eighties, no less, Libby adds.

Neither of them brings up Angela.

Angela stopped talking to Sithara in third year. She stopped talking to Libby too, when Libby tried to ask her about it. They never found out why. Sithara would see Angela coming towards her sometimes in the hallways of the law faculty and would run away to avoid bumping into her. The rejection stung like a breakup.

We know everything about each other, I guess, Libby tells Mojdeh.

Not everything, Sithara says.

Oh, really? Libby rocks back on the legs of the barstool and waits. What secrets do you have that I don't know about?

Mojdeh laughs. Her laugh is at odds with her exquisite face, almost a guffaw.

Sithara hesitates, embarrassed to have someone listening in. Seeing Libby always brings the past back in full force. There's a version of herself she can only ever be around her oldest friend.

She considers it – painting the picture of that cold morning when she and Suri led a car off the road. Telling Libby about the real cause of the crash that rocked their school. Sharing the violence that is inside of her too. Libby and Mojdeh look at her expectantly.

Sithara just shrugs. You're right, Lib, I guess you do know it all.

Once more, Mojdeh looks at Sithara uneasily. She walks away to the other end of the bar to serve a customer who had pointedly cleared his throat. It's not even the hardest secret Sithara has to share.

—

Sithara manages to be honest with Libby right before they stand to leave.

Paul got out today.

Libby presses her hand to her mouth. Two other bartenders are working now and Mojdeh has all more or less joined them. She polishes glasses, part of the conversation.

My ex-husband was in jail. The words escape from her mouth like a slip at the top of the stairs. He beat me unconscious three years ago. My mum found me.

Mojdeh shakes her head, grim. She reaches behind her for the vodka and pours them all a shot, maintaining eye contact with Sithara while they cheers.

The vodka coats her mouth like gasoline.

I've missed him, she says, giving up her greatest secret. Now it is outside of her body, living in the same world as her daughter. Her chest stings. Sithara only ever realises the full truth of something after saying it aloud.

There is nothing good for you, with him, Libby says. Her voice cracks. There is nothing good for you, with a man like that.

Sithara looks away, stares at the ground. The pain in Libby's face is unbearable.

You might not be able to stop loving him, Libby says, but you need to remember what he did to you. If you don't, you'll never get over him, Thara. Not really. Libby tries to catch Sithara's eyes again, and when she fails, she takes Sithara's chin in her hands and lifts her face towards her.

Then she presses their foreheads together in the middle of the bar like she is trying to will her out of love.

I need to get home, Sithara says softly.

She and Libby tip Mojdeh and walk to the car park. Sithara wants to shake all the feeling out of her body.

I'm so sorry. Do you think he's going to try to get in touch with you? With Annie?

No, no, he wouldn't do that, Sithara lies.

They hug. Sithara whispers thank you into Libby's ear and waves goodbye, wishing she could alter her friend's view of her. Or scrub it clean.

Mojdeh finds Sithara before she leaves. She pulls a pack of cigarettes out of the pocket of her jeans and offers one to Sithara, who shakes her head.

You remind me of my amma a little, she tells Mojdeh.

I hope that's a good thing, Mojdeh replies. Sithara is silent.

The sooner you forget him, the less you'll hate yourself. Mojdeh's voice is brittle. She shrugs as if to say, *that's all.*

Sithara keeps an eye on Mojdeh as she drives away, watching her hair burn orange in the waning light.

On big days, Sithara tries to write Suri letters. She wants to fill him in on all that has happened. She wants to apologise. She wants him to know things about his niece. The intense face Annie makes when she is listening, the way she wakes up before her alarm and sits in her bed, looking out the window. That she gets anxious when she is still for too long. How she concentrates with her body. How her favourite thing to eat for breakfast is tinned sardines with lots of lemon on toast, just like him.

But today Sithara can only stare at empty paper, recalling the rage and disappointment on Suri's face the day he walked out of her office.

Sithara knows that Maude Aunty tries with Amma. That she yearns to talk to her about Suri. Amma has Suri's address; she has seen it in a notebook by the phone. She wonders if Amma sits and looks at it, if all the things she also cannot say collect in her mind like leaves at the bottom of a teacup.

She stays alert to ways she can bring Amma around. There's a chef on TV Amma and Annie like, who Sithara thinks might be gay. Amma has frowned at a few of his jokes in the past, but she hasn't said anything cruel. Sithara will point out how brilliant and creative he is, and Amma will nod and agree.

Months ago, she found Amma reading an article about a state in the US legalising same-sex civil unions. She was gripping the paper tightly, crunching the corners of it into broken ruffles. She flinched when Sithara saw her with it and tried to hide the headline. For a single penetrating moment it felt like Suri was in the room with them, pushing his glasses up his nose and leaning over Amma's shoulder to keep reading.

—

Amma and Annie are watching *Holmes* when Sithara walks in.

Happy birthday, Ammi. Sorry I'm late.

Annie leaps up to help Sithara with the mango pudding. Since taking up gymnastics, she has started wearing her hair in slick ponytails and buns. Sithara loves seeing all of her daughter's face, the ears that make her look like a cartoon mouse. Amma pulls bowls and spoons from the cupboard. She seems preoccupied. She's never cheerful on birthdays.

While they eat dessert, Annie talks about her friend Emily who plays the violin. She has tried a few times now to make a case for violin lessons on top of gymnastics; Sithara is sure this is because of The Corrs and makes a mental note to hide their CDs. She tries to politely explain her position – that almost any other badly played instrument would sound better than a badly played violin – without hurting Annie's feelings.

Once Annie is in bed, Sithara returns to Amma's house alone. She brings a bottle of sherry. It is the only kind of alcohol she has ever seen Amma drink. They sit on Amma's deck with blankets wrapped around their shoulders.

You'll be sixty next year, Sithara says, looking at her unlined face.

Amma has kept an approximation of the haircut she gave

herself when Appa died. It's been short for so many years now that Sithara struggles to recall her any other way. She used to think getting rid of her hair was Amma punishing herself. Whatever it was, it stuck.

The sun sets over the garden, making everything soft and delicate. The cicadas roar. The bougainvillea Amma planted when they first moved in has exploded into joyful violet stars. The air between Sithara and Amma is full.

Were they ever able to speak freely? About Annie they are always frank, about each other or Suri they are helpless. Yet the moment feels like it begs for some kind of honesty.

Did you ever think about dating again? Sithara asks.

Amma looks alarmed. She shakes her head.

You're so young, Amma. There's still time.

Amma pulls a sour face. I'm not *so* young.

Sithara nods and sits in silence, retreating rather than risk spoiling the evening. She thinks about Mojdeh following her out, about how comforting it was to talk with her and Libby, about how little of the rest of her life feels like that.

Would you come if we moved? Sithara asks.

Moved? Moved where?

I don't know. I don't think I want to practise law anymore. Maybe I want to teach it. I feel lonely.

Lonely? You have us.

But I don't have friends. I don't really have anyone that thinks like me.

This seems to strike something with Amma. She nods.

Murmurs her assent. Nods once more. I missed that too, when we left.

Sithara feels the warmth of the sherry spread through her whole body. She and Amma are relating to one another.

Exactly. That's why I'm saying you could meet someone!

Now Amma chuckles as though Sithara is speaking nonsense.

There was a proposal, Amma says.

Her words strike the air like a drum.

A proposal?

Yes. She looks out into the garden. A long time ago, there was another man who wanted to be with me. But it was too late; I was already in love with your appa. She sips her sherry and closes her eyes.

After Appa died, this man came back and asked me to marry him. He said I was too young to be a widow, that I needed someone to take care of me. The usual nonsense.

Sithara should have known that Amma's beauty didn't exist in a vacuum, that of course there were others, regardless of whether Sithara saw them.

But how did he find you? Sithara asks, picturing a large squat man with a moustache, the strongest possible contrast to her appa.

Amma turns and considers Sithara, as though judging whether to trust her.

Well, she says.

Amma!

It was Edward Uncle. Now will you leave me alone?

Aiyo, Sithara whistles.

Amma is stoic, refusing to engage. The sun disappears like water being poured over fire.

Your brother-in-law! You had brothers fighting over you and you never told us? She claps her hands.

Wicked girl, Amma says, frowning.

Sithara raises her glass. It's not me who's the wicked one.

Despite her best efforts to appear unaffected, a smile pulls at the corner of Amma's lips, betraying her.

Sithara looks at their big house across the garden and thinks again of Suri. It is like death, this gulf between them, this severing.

Amma doesn't notice Sithara's shift. If you moved, I would move too, she tells her. I would go to Melbourne to be with Maude.

Sithara looks at Amma to check she heard correctly.

You would leave us?

Amma squirms just a little under Sithara's gaze.

I want the same things you do. I want to be with my friend.

Something returns to Sithara. A sense that she has had since she was very young, of being a disappointment to Amma. The memory of letting her down and letting Suri get hurt and never being forgiven for it. Although there is a part of Sithara that hears Amma and knows her wish is reasonable, there is a larger part which is angry.

You're being selfish, Sithara tells her. The hurt look on Amma's face is immediately gratifying. Sithara snatches her half-full glass and takes it inside. Amma follows.

You don't need me like you once did. You'll be okay.

Have you thought about what this will do to Annie? How much she'll miss you?

Of course I have, Amma says. But that girl is hard, isn't she? She has had to be.

It stings, as intended.

Sithara faces away, washing the dishes. She hasn't considered being a mother without her own. As long as there has been Annie there has been Amma. Suri's absence shimmers in the air.

Josephina
1989, Invercargill

When she was newly widowed, Josephina's life was concentrated into the seconds after she woke up. In these moments she would lie graveyard still.

She was unable to break the habit of sleeping on her side of the bed. She would wake in a daze, open her eyes and notice the light striving through the corners of the blinds, her hands clenched, as always, around the top of the duvet. She would wonder whether Ravi had slept well, what he might like to eat for breakfast. These were moments when her lover was still within reach.

And then she would move just an inch, notice the stretch of empty mattress beside her, and the horizon would disappear. Ravi was gone. Years without him unravelled in front of her.

Ravi and Josephina had been discussing plans for a trip back home. It was still a year away – the cost to take all four of them was so big they had to work backwards. An Easter trip, cheaper than flying at Christmas. Ravi was excited to tell the children.

He got up to make her a cup of tea; she was thinking about what to cook. That was her life before – holiday plans and dinner. And then his hand shot out to clasp the side of the bench and he yelled out her name and she realised she had never seen him experience terror. She caught him as his head dropped onto his chest and that was it. He was plucked right out of his life.

Josephina held him and sank to the ground. She listened to his breath, checked his pulse. It was a reflex, she already knew he was dead. He looked the same as Pātti. And then something got loose. So much sound came from her body, poured out of her stomach and hit the walls and reverberated back. She searched for him, trying to fill up the space he left. It went on and on. Her cries called the neighbours and the ambulance and the police.

By the time they came she was silent. She can still remember one of the ambulance drivers trying to comfort her, saying she was probably numb and that was okay. How inaccurate. Josephina wasn't numb. She had been skinned. She felt everything.

Six years later, it is only Ravi's hair that appears in her dreams. She sees the soft triangle at the nape of his neck, clipped too close to curl, as he speaks to the children. The ringlets on top of his head, murmuring, while he wraps his arms around Josephina, pressing his face to her stomach and breathing her in.

Sometimes it is his hairline, a glimpse of his forehead. This image will be so realistic behind her closed eyes that she will hear his laugh again. She will shudder out of sleep, wondering if someone planted lavender outside her window in the night.

She does not dream of his face.

The ceiling above Josephina is heavy and the air in her room is cold. They have a fireplace that warms the whole house when lit correctly, but Sithara and Ravi were the only ones who were any good at lighting it.

Today is the first day Josephina will be truly alone. What would happen if she stopped time? If she allowed herself to stay in bed. If she didn't get up and make the milk rice for Suri and instead dissolved, merging into the sheets, atoms isolating themselves from one another and reforming as cotton, her son crashing upstairs to discover only an empty bed and a dark room?

Josephina finds Suri in the kitchen, crouched over his open suitcase. He is moving to Dunedin today, where he will study English. It is not as good as law or medicine, but Josephina has given up trying to change her son's mind. He most likely got his love of books from her anyway.

Your shirts are drying in the hot water cupboard, she tells him.

She reaches into the pantry to pull out ingredients for pol sambol. Edward sends her Maldive fish by the kilogram; she had to buy a chest freezer to contain all the food parcels he started shipping her after Ravi died. She fries curry leaves and chilli and drains them, letting them cool. She pounds the rest of the ingredients together, lamenting as always the lack of fresh coconuts.

Come, eat. Then we will leave, she tells Suri, setting two plates on the table.

Suri stands, hovering around the back of the chair.

Ammi, I need to talk to you.

She sits and looks up at him, waiting. The kitchen smells of fresh-cut lime. Yesterday she bought lilies and arranged them in a vase on the table. At the time it seemed celebratory, but now they look sad, like an omen. Their orange centres have already dropped, littering the table with fine dust.

Suri is nice-looking – both her children are. He has always been more delicate and easily hurt than Sithara, but that never seemed like something that was in Josephina's power to change. She has tried to treat them both the same.

Suri used to appear in their bedroom on Saturday mornings and make them watch while he enacted scenes from the books he was reading. He was always shy with strangers, but at home he was cheeky like his appa.

Josephina spoons pol sambol onto the side of his plate. Suri doesn't speak and instead sits, helping himself to milk rice. She eats, recalling the pain of abruptly having to cook for three people instead of four. For weeks she set Ravi's place at the table, frantically removing the leftover cutlery before the children noticed. She doesn't even know how to cook for one.

One death is really so many deaths. The day she told Suri his appa was gone he had blinked and looked around surprised, like he didn't know where he was. They were standing in the hallway of the hospital where Ravi had worked. Then his face closed. She tried to hold him but he stepped out of her arms, shaking his head. She wanted more than anything to cut out the part of Suri that hurt and carry it.

On the morning of Ravi's funeral, Josephina got drunk. She took the arrack that Maude sent for Ravi's last birthday to her bedroom and poured herself three shots, one after the other. She brushed her hair and washed her face and felt herself lift away from her body. She drained the rest of the bottle in the church car park like a teenager.

At the service, Josephina blazed in white. The western tradition of wearing black on a day that was already so dark felt unholy, so she ignored it. She picked a white blouse and loose white pants, island clothes, and walked down the aisle with her hands resting on her children's shoulders. Ravi's colleagues whispered to one another when they saw her. She dressed like Ravi had the day she'd met him, serene and presumptuous in her spot under the banyan tree. She told herself to keep her chin up even as tears made the church around her swim.

Everything was wrapped in cotton wool. Josephina remained alert only to the needs of her children. The whole family came from Colombo. Maude arranged the food for the afternoon tea. Nisha walked around making people smile. Karnan made coffee. Edward kept his eyes glued to Josephina. He brought her a glass of water while everyone ate in the church function room. As soon as the water touched the back of her throat, she felt sick.

Edward wasted no time trying to take care of her. That very night he offered to pay for all of them to come home. He and Chootie were divorced, with no children. He said he had an empty house, enough money to give the children anything they wanted. Josephina shook her head, claiming she couldn't bear to destabilise Sithara and Suri further, but it was only half true.

The thought of going back to Ravi's home, without him, was unbearable. Leaving New Zealand would mean leaving the last place she saw him, the kitchen where he took his last breath. He was still here.

If she stood in the hospital foyer and squinted hard enough, she could see him walking out. In the cosmetics aisle of the supermarket she could picture his hand reaching for a new toothbrush. It was easy to conjure him. In the weeks after the funeral Josephina would drive herself to different places and just stand there, listening.

A room of sombre people in black ate brandy snaps and apologised to her children. She watched the rituals of death play out. The old feelings of wanting to claw at the world around her returned. It was as though all the happiness she was ever going to feel had now passed. She cursed Ravi for dying before her. Everyone said that life was short, and for her husband, it was. But for Josephina, drunk at his funeral, wishing the tidal wave of death would crash in and take her too, life felt long.

✦

They head for the copper-coloured hills. Invercargill falls away behind them and the roads have texture again. Bob Dylan sings 'Tombstone Blues'. All of Suri's music sounds like dirges. Josephina prefers music with a little bit of life in it, like Prince. Suri hums along and nods his head.

Sithara's flatmates moved out at just the right time for Suri to move in. Josephina assumed Suri would go into one of the halls, that he would want to meet new people and find his own friends to flat with, but her children seem to prefer to live together.

I've read most of the texts we're meant to study this term already, he says.

What are they?

The morning sun is vicious. It shoots into their eyes. She unfolds the visor on the ceiling of the car to shield Suri from it.

King Lear, The Turn of the Screw, Dr Jekyll and Mr Hyde.

Suri reads on a pouf by the fire, chin resting in his hands, knees pressed together. He maintains this position for hours. He looks like a heron. He reads with eyes like polished silver.

Recently, Josephina has come to suspect that Sithara has a boyfriend. She is sure she heard a man's voice in the background when she called yesterday morning. And that was not the first time.

When Sithara moved to Dunedin four years ago, she was anxious, unsettled. She came home every other weekend. Then she vanished. She stopped visiting, stopped calling Suri, seemed distracted when they called her. She could hear it in Sithara's voice – the sound of her daughter belonging to someone. She tried to imagine the kind of man who would steal away her time like this.

Amma, Suri says, turning down the music. I wanted to tell you something back at the house, but I didn't know how.

Again, she waits. She didn't feel nervous in the kitchen, but she wonders now what could be so difficult to say.

You need to know that, Suri shakes his head and takes one hand off the steering wheel, pressing his wrist to his mouth.

I'm not upset with you, Suri, she says. Medicine or law

would have been better, of course, but you have to do what makes you happy.

Suri gives a strange laugh. Josephina adjusts herself in her seat. She is uncomfortable, guilty. She didn't realise she had made her disappointment so obvious.

I'm not talking about school, he says.

He falls silent again. They're over an hour into the drive, coming up to Clinton, according to the map she keeps unfolded on her lap. Although they have come this way before, Josephina feels safer being able to track exactly where they are. All around them are empty fields, the boundaries of each marked with fences, posts with wire between them that are invisible from this far away.

The hills are loud with fierce yellow gorse. The trees are bare, naked branches reaching out towards one another, their heads the only part of them with leaves. Josephina never sees farmhouses when they are driving these roads. Just barns and endless fields. There is so much *space* in this country. Barely any refugees, and all this room.

A year ago, Josephina had a short affair. With her neighbour. He was the father of a friend of Sithara's. A widower himself, of course. Josephina wouldn't have been able to engage in anything as immoral as adultery.

His name was Ryan Pearson. A Welshman with grey flickering through his chest hair. It happened so unexpectedly.

Josephina knew he had always liked her, but his attention made her uncomfortable, until one day it didn't.

One day it made her feel her body was heavy with lust like a water balloon. He knocked on her door to offer eggs from his chickens and she pulled him inside by the collar of his shirt. The first kiss made her feel like weeping but then her mind went blank.

Ryan didn't speak, he just looked up at her in awe. They didn't share meals, didn't go out in public. He would buy her groceries and leave them in the kitchen. Sometimes they would fall asleep on the couch. Sometimes they would talk about their children.

It was a surprise to find she could enjoy sex with a man she didn't love, strange to be given what she needed without being asked for much in return. It was sex and companionship – immense, essential things, but they felt easy. How incredible that more than one man in her life would be kind to her.

Ryan made love to Josephina like he deserved her. His sweat dripped onto her face when he was on top. She surprised both of them by licking his neck one afternoon and they had to stop to laugh. This was when they heard Suri's key in the front door.

There was nothing for it but to run upstairs. Ryan stayed locked in Josephina's bedroom until the next morning when Suri left again. He didn't complain. But the fear of her son finding another man in his parents' bedroom was enough for Josephina to put a stop to it. She had her memories. They went back to being neighbours.

Suri pulls the car slowly off the road and parks by a wooden picnic table. Josephina marks their spot on the map with a pencil. They sit opposite one another and she lifts out a thermos full of tea and two beef sandwiches wrapped in paper.

Suri sits beside her and pours tea into the lid of the thermos, offering it to her. She has come to enjoy the cold, to appreciate the crispness of Southland in winter. The steam fogs both their spectacles and mother and son peer at each other through the gaps in their vision.

Layers of fat gently enveloped Josephina after Ravi died. It took some time for her to notice. She kept telling herself she was just wearing fresh pants, shrunk to their original size by the wash. They all left painful button-shaped indents on her stomach. After a few months of struggling to sit without needing to slightly undo her zipper, she gave in and bought bigger sizes.

It felt like a rite of passage. Men on the street stopped noticing her. It didn't change when she cut her hair off, only when she put on weight. It was so basic it felt almost embarrassing. She should have done it years ago.

Suri puts both his hands on the table between them. Amma, he says again, plaintive.

She starts to get annoyed with him now, to wonder why he can't just spit it out. Her gaze hardens even as she tells herself to be soft.

He looks as though he already regrets what he's going to say. His face is a wrong turn, a plunge into water too deep.

Amma, I'm gay.

Josephina's blood cools.

I've known since I was a child. I didn't know how to tell you. It's not bad — it isn't a bad thing.

She stares at Suri. The sky is a bright blue bowl above them. The future murmurs just out of hearing like distant thunder. Why is he telling her this? What does he want? She shakes her head, trying to rewind, hoping he will just suck his confession back in so they can both pretend it didn't happen.

In her head she hears Suri's desperation in Sigiriya, his pleading, as he burst out of dark toilet stalls and rushed towards her. She packs the sandwiches into her handbag and clutches it to her chest, stares at the car and the road behind him. Suri slides his hands towards her but stops when he sees the revulsion on her face.

Okay Ammi, he says. He pours her tea back into the thermos and stands to head back to the car. This gesture of acceptance wakes her up. She wriggles up off the table and blocks his way. He looks nothing like the fat silly boy she raised and loved, who grew tall and serious in their house of grief. He twists from her, averting her eyes.

The cheek of it, she shoves his chest, the cheek of it, to not even look at her when he has ruined so many things, when he's brought it all back, the smacking sound of Chintu's little knees meeting the ground, Sithara looking at her like she had become a stranger, Josephina's terrible lie.

She pushes Suri again but she feels her own mother's finger pushing back at her and it bullies her mind into words. They are right behind her mouth and they want to get out. He has already buckled like a tin can. He looks so drained and so wounded, she doesn't need to say a thing. She tries not to.

Thank God your appa is not alive to hear this.

They arrive at Sithara's flat just before eleven. It is smaller than Josephina remembers. Two white boys are smoking cigarettes outside. They have moustaches and long curly hair cut short on the sides, giving them manicured manes.

She gets out and opens the boot, lifting Suri's boxes and throwing them onto the pavement. The boys don't rise to help her. Suri escapes as soon as the car stops and bangs on the front door, calling for Sithara. The boys lounge like she and Suri are not even there. Their youth and apathy needles her. Sithara comes to the door in loose shorts and a sports bra.

Can you guys get off my porch, please? she says to the smoking boys, irritated. Paul's not here and I don't know when he will be.

So his name is Paul. Josephina looks at Sithara to see if she has noticed her own slip up, but she is just standing there, half-dressed, staring daggers at the boys. They laugh, then do as she says. They drop half-smoked cigarettes onto the ground beside Suri's feet. Josephina's fingers itch to save them from the dirt and finish them off.

Sithara pulls Suri in for a hug. They hold still, framed by the peeling white paint of the doorway. He is only slightly taller than she is. He hunches and rests his head on the soft pillow of hair on her shoulder. Josephina can tell that Sithara knows, and has for some time. She feels like she has been stabbed in the back.

Amma, I'll take those, Sithara says, running over. You go inside and sit down. She kisses Josephina on the cheek and Josephina flinches. She makes herself follow Sithara into the house.

While Suri is setting up his bed and Sithara is in the bathroom, she leaves.

✦

If something were to happen to Josephina, no one would know for days. Her children have no other family here. They would be orphans.

Josephina really believed she had left the acidic emptiness of Singapore behind her. That she had built herself a family. She pulls up outside the house and thoughts too awful to look directly at, shuffle into her head and assemble themselves. The street is empty, as it always is. She contemplates knocking on Ryan's door.

When they ended things it took Josephina some time to forget the way his large hands enveloped her naked back, the way his forehead creased when he listened to her speak. They discussed the end of the affair as much as they discussed the start of it, which is to say, they didn't. It wouldn't be unimaginable to begin again. It would be easy to lose herself in the immolation of his desire. But maybe all of that is in the past for a reason. Josephina has never allowed herself to believe she deserves nice things just for the sake of having them.

After an hour of staring at the house, she goes inside. Her shoes echo on the wooden floor of the hallway. The sound bounces back, taunting her. She looks at the baby chandelier above her head and remembers Ravi pointing to it with a flourish, using it as proof of what grand times they were going to have here.

Suri has stripped his bed and left his sheets in a pile at the end for Josephina to wash. There are neat towers of schoolbooks on his desk. His walls are mostly bare, the wardrobe gutted, his drawers empty save for some pants sent by Inesh and Suji when he was still small. She rubs the beaded satin between her fingers, the diamond-shaped mirrors look up like eyes. He is a stranger to her now.

Being an outsider in this country is hard enough without being gay. She grimaces. It hurts to even think the word in her head. She wanted an easy life for her children. She wanted them to get married and make their own families. She wanted them to feel like they could relax. She shudders at the thought of what he will get up to in Dunedin, away from her, with men.

Josephina dreads her next confession. The words coming out of her mouth, even in the safety of the confession box, will sting. They will be barbed with her own guilt. She's the one who brought Chintu into the house and started all of this.

She may have to lie, layering sins one after another, to say that it is not Suri, but some nephew back home she is worried about. That it is still an uncertain thing, only suspicion. Not a declaration made in broad daylight. She can't bear the embarrassment of anyone knowing *this*.

She gathers the bed linen mechanically, turning her head to the side so she can see over the top of it, placing her feet carefully down each step. When she gets to the bottom she keeps walking. She bypasses the laundry and goes straight outside. She lifts the lid of the ash bin and stuffs Suri's linen in, pushing her arms and half of her torso down to make sure not one scrap of white pokes out.

Piece by piece, she removes everything she can carry from Suri's room. She wedges what she can into the bin and leaves what she can't fit in the sitting room. Comic books and diaries pile up on Suri's reading pouf, on top of old library notices and school reports. Taking his desk to the roadside is less easy; she tries to turn it to get it down the stairs and it skids out of her reach. Its sharp corner leaves a hole in the wall. Close to defeat, Josephina stops and stares at it.

He's known since he was a child. Is she really so oblivious? Josephina recalls Raana and Margaret. The way they always sat so close. Raana's commitment to her own anonymity even in the back room. Inesh and Ranil? Were they like this? Has she really been sleepwalking through so much of life?

Once the desk is sitting on the street she drags the ash bin to the centre of the garden, pushes small bits of kindling around the linens and lights two corners. Yellow flames lick the air. The urge to put the fire out grabs Josephina but she ignores it. She locks her fingers together over her belly to restrain herself. When she eventually does pour water over the flames, sludge collects at the bottom of the bin in thick pools.

She wanted to kill Chintu. She actually wanted to hurt that small, tortured boy when she thought he had hurt Suri. But he was barely older than Suri himself, and now she figures there was something unnatural, yes, but mutual between them.

Inside, she turns her attention to the fireplace. She closes her eyes and tries to remember what Ravi's hands looked like twisting newspaper, breaking wood into smaller and smaller pieces. She builds the kindling up from her memories. She can see the glow of the fire reflected in his beautiful black eyes. When it is hot enough for a log to catch, she starts stuffing her son's childhood into it.

She closes the door after each new piece. Every last trace of his childish handwriting disappears. She watches his school reports evaporate. Comments from his English teacher about his writing talent catch light and wither in front of her. She burns his baby photos. They melt with a blue flame and then turn into wisps of plastic and paper.

She imagines Suri coming home and finding his things gone. She could tell him that clothing moths ate holes in everything he left behind. That there was borer in the desk. That a pipe burst and sewerage emptied out over everything.

What good would any of these explanations do? She will never get her son back. Perhaps she will stay silent and allow the room's emptiness to speak for her.

Annie

2017, Auckland

The sound of bodies hitting the mat is like a lullaby to Annie. Light thuds, sharp exhales of pride when someone lands a strike exactly where they intended. Bare feet shuffle to switch kick, pairs change position to run a drill again. The hall has high ceilings and big windows. Light pours in from above, like a cathedral. It smells like liniment. Annie stalks the room observing her students.

Hunter and Frances drive into the city every Saturday morning from Waiuku. They're best friends. When Frances started class they wore jeans. Now they wear trackpants and secure their hair in tight braids. Annie listens to the pair talking their way through a take down before they run it again. She moves on to another group.

Annie spent the first part of class demonstrating faints, explaining how they create confusion. She's found this to be the best structure for her teaching – that collective interest is better sustained if she lays out class objectives before allowing students to practise. There are always questions. They're usually expressions of anxiety rather than genuine queries. She wonders how different teaching children would be, what kind of child might need to learn these skills.

She's just finished three hard months on a German co-production. There were horses, a bit of driving, and an executive producer who kept adding fights. There was a stunt where she chipped her way out of a frozen lake of ice with a hammer. The director called take after take until Annie's lips turned blue.

She runs a queer-focused self-defence class. It's in its second year. The course is twelve weeks total, in a community centre up the road from her flat. When she first rented the hall, her intention was to coach actors in stunt training. This was selfish, a way of making her own job a little easier.

On set she's often asked to teach actors the initial moves of a fight. Most of this is just explaining that the person pretending to take the hit is the one doing the real work. It takes male actors hours to understand; they're so easily distracted, they forget the choreography. She thought that running her own class teaching stunt basics to actors would be like laying groundwork. And then one night she was out with her girlfriend Nia and they were followed home.

They were leaving a restaurant and decided to walk rather

than spend the extra money on an Uber. Nia was tipsy and laughing. She was so beautiful under the light of the streetlamp that Annie couldn't stop herself from kissing her. Her lips tasted like sangria.

When Annie pulled away there were two white men staring at them. One had on a brown fedora, he was shorter than Nia, the same height as Annie. But the other was twice the size. He had a thick neck and his smile didn't reach his eyes. He looked curious rather than angry, but he was standing so close that Annie could see his eyelashes. They were jagged, like he had cut the ends of them with scissors.

Annie and Nia started to walk away, but when the men fell into step beside them they ran. They held hands and didn't look back. Annie could hear the rattle and smash of Nia's brass earrings fall out and hit the pavement, her own breathless panting. They ran so fast that Annie felt sick. When they got home, Nia bolted the doors of their house and put furniture in front as an extra precaution. Neither of them slept. The next day Annie rebranded her class.

She teaches her students how to block punches, how to fall in a way that doesn't damage their joints or their brain. She tries to keep things practical. She knows that if the worst does happen, the best anyone who isn't used to fighting can hope for is to minimise damage to themselves. She directs their focus away from causing damage to others.

Two girls she knows a little from outside class, Maaza and Persephone, have been pushing Annie for lessons in fighting back. Maaza reminds Annie so much of herself that it is painful. Her shoulders and back ripple with muscles. She laughs too loud. When she successfully masters her technique she insists on running it again with a doggedness no other student can match.

Persephone asked for lessons in how to cause damage to someone's windpipe on day one. Her front tooth is turning black and she wears gloves she never takes off. She sent Annie an email reiterating her request a week later and Annie ignored it, but offered the spare room in their flat. Persephone declined. When the day came to learn a couple of attack basics, she arrived early.

It was the same last year. Some students come because it seems prudent to do so. Others come because they have a score to settle. Annie loves to watch them grow more and more precise. The air in the room becomes limitless. Annie's own ambitions expand alongside her students.

It is her favourite thing, watching a room full of queer people learn that their bodies are capable of more than they believed possible. They start to learn that size is not the only determinant of force, that senses can be honed, execution refined to the point where a yearning to do damage is the only thing that matters. But blood is not the only point of combat. Knowing you can protect yourself makes music louder and drinks stronger.

When class comes to an end Annie encourages everyone to stay for five minutes and reflect on their progress. She gives Maaza the keys to lock up and walks out into the sun to where Nia is waiting, chewing the inside of her cheek with anxiety.

Nia is Fijian. She's an engineer. On their first date she said, *God your ears are big*, and ordered for them both. They had planned only to have dinner, but dinner led to dessert, which led to a walk along a stormy beach, which led to the two of them pulling up at Annie's flat and making out in the car.

It was less pressure than going inside. Annie felt like they were suspended in thick amber, frozen in the triumph of a perfect first date. Nia is interesting, cute and open-minded. She is similar to Annie in a way that is intoxicating. Annie knows Nia. She knows the things Nia will laugh at and the questions that will break her heart. The first time Nia spoke to her, Annie felt as if she had heard her voice before. On their one-year anniversary they moved in together.

Nia cooks. She makes poached eggs every Friday morning and spends weekends roasting tomatoes and pickling whatever vegetables are in season. She often falls asleep with candles burning. When Annie has to work late, her girlfriend being burned alive at home is all she can think about.

Annie mows the lawns and does their washing. She runs a dehumidifier every weekend in the lounge. She is learning how to share a space, how to be part of a team. How to work better together than apart.

Nia grew up with cousins and aunties and uncles. Regular trips back to Suva to spend time with more family. Her relatives in Aotearoa welcomed Annie into the fold with plates of food and open invitations to every weekend get-together. The ones back home don't know that Nia is queer.

Maybe because her own childhood was largely a happy one, Nia has never been able to understand why Annie speaks so cruelly about her father. She says it happened long ago, that people change. One night she told Annie that if she didn't forgive him she would never really heal. It was heavy with the suggestion that if Annie never *healed*, Nia wouldn't stick around. And that is why, in an effort to not lose the only partner she has ever loved, Annie has agreed to sit down and talk with Paul.

Nia parks outside the cafe and squeezes Annie's hand. Annie is scared she will cry if she makes eye contact, so she just squeezes back and hops out of the car.

Her mum texted with his number three seconds after Annie asked for it. Still, it took her weeks to message. She kept staring at it, sitting right there in her phone like a bomb. She studied the shape of each digit, hoping they would reveal something to her. She couldn't easily recall Paul's face. She knew he had light eyes. She remembers him being tall, but so is everyone to a seven-year-old.

They are meeting in a cafe on the North Shore. Annie

mashes the ice cubes in her coffee with the butt of a metal straw, grinding each one carefully into shards.

There have been low moments in her life when Annie has tried to look for her father online. Paul Fischer is mentioned in two articles, both reports from court cases. He's had a derelict Facebook profile for a few years. In the display picture his face is largely obscured by a cap. He has his arm thrown around the shoulder of a young boy she doesn't know. His outward-facing personality looks jolly but there is something unsteady, like he has practised it. His likes are listed as 'reggae' and 'cars'. He could be any middle-aged white man.

The other customers here are either elderly – she watched one of them insist on extra hot coffee and then complain to the barista when it burned her mouth – or young mothers with toddlers, making forced conversation over gluten-free toast.

One mum sits at her table reading the newspaper. Her children look about two and three years old. Strapped into the seats of their double stroller, passing a plastic spoon back and forth. Monica has a baby now, Annie's goddaughter Florence. When Annie visits Monica, she picks Florence up and presses her nose to her hair. She smells like dough the moment it becomes bread.

She's glad Nia dropped her off early. It gives her time to assess the environment, to calm down a little. To do some of the breathing exercises Nia taught her. She closes her eyes to recall the comforting state of freedom and possibility she finds in class. But she only finds childhood memories she thought she'd forgotten, standing, then sitting on the pavement with her mum one day after a dentist appointment. Paul was supposed to pick them up. He never showed.

Paul and her mum's reunion didn't last more than a year. But that was long enough for Annie to lose faith in the one parent she admitted to having. Her mum called her when they broke up and fell silent over the phone as though she was waiting for Annie to say *I told you so.*

Annie didn't. She asked if Paul had hurt her and her mum just laughed, which distressed Annie. It made her feel like she had imagined the whole thing. She so badly wanted to ask why they got back together, what it was about being with him that was so good, but the words dried up in her mouth. She was scared of the answer being something to do with love, of the implication that love could be more important than physical safety.

Sometimes when Annie and her mum argue, Annie will feel the impulse to tear their relationship to pieces. To sever ties. To punish her for putting both of them through it.

The scrape of the chair opposite lifts Annie out of her coffee. She leans back slowly, resting her elbow on the booth behind and narrowing her eyes. Paul is standing above her, his smile stiff. He seems to be waiting for her to get up and hug him. She slides her fingernail between her two front teeth and picks, staring.

The skin under his eyes has sagged and he has dark spots on his hands. His hair has almost completely disappeared from the crown of his head. His nose might have grown. The bulb at the end of it is thick.

Hi, Annie, he says, forcing the table onto an angle as he sits.

She scans his features against her own before she can help herself. Different eyes, different chin, different face shape, same forehead. He is tall, somewhere over six foot. He could have given her that, at least.

You look good. He nods.

Annie corrects the line of the table with one hand and snorts. She's in the best shape of her life.

Where do you stay? she asks.

Greenhithe, for now, Paul says. It was nice to hear from you.

His voice stirs something that is difficult to acknowledge. She hates him, but she also feels, uncomfortably, like she wants him to know she is successful. In his eyes she hopes to find something good, qualities that are worthy. If there is nothing good about Paul then what did her mum do it for?

Your mum tells me you have a girlfriend? he says.

When did you last speak to my mum?

We talk on the phone now and then.

Do you have a problem with me having a girlfriend?

Not at all, Paul says, grinning like a salesman and spreading his hands wide. All I want is for you to be happy.

Right, Annie says.

He sighs. Look, Annie.

She hates when men say *look*.

I've changed. I don't know how much you've been told. He frowns and rubs the edge of the table. But it hasn't been easy for me.

Annie has to assume he's talking about prison. Or maybe the meth. It was Gran who dumped that information on her.

I wish you'd get to know me, Paul says. I was stupid back then. It's different now. He nods as he talks, like he is encouraging himself.

Annie wonders if the stupidity he is referring to is the time he kicked her mum unconscious.

He tries to catch her eye, hopeful for confirmation or a smile, but she avoids him and continues breathing, slowly, in and out through her nose. She feels her pulse rising. The room around them quivers.

Stupid. What an interesting word to use, Annie says.

The waitress interrupts, asking if they want to order anything else and Annie shakes her head. Paul says the coffee was delicious and his tone is like syrup. Annie wants to stab the metal straw into her ears to block it out. He stands and walks over to the counter, nodding at the barista and complimenting her so emphatically that she is obliged to smile back, to thank him. The babies and their mum are gone.

The sky is cloudless, the air shimmering. She follows Paul

out to the car park. His car is at the end furthest from the cafe. Nia is still sitting in her own car across the road. She promised they would get ice cream together afterwards, talk things over, decompress. Initially Annie was touched by Nia's support, but now she feels like she is here to spy, to make sure Annie shows patience, or forgiveness or something like it.

Paul bounces on the balls of his feet while he walks, jolting up suddenly and then down again. He turns to say goodbye to Annie and all she can focus on are his eyes. They're a washed-out green. She has never seen a colour this unappealing. They're so light that the black ring around them looks fake, like a coloured contact lens. Paul breathes out slowly, as though readying himself. Annie waits, the sun hot on her cheeks.

No more bullshit. I want us to move forwards. I forgive you, Annie, for testifying against me.

Paul forgives *her*. Annie throws her head back and laughs. He reaches out for a hug at the same time. The gesture is so bizarre that Annie considers he may be high. He steps closer and she doesn't have time to modulate her response. She grabs him by the shoulders and drops her chin, launches herself upwards and slams her forehead into his nose.

Paul stumbles back, landing on the bonnet of his car. He reaches both hands up to his face. Blood pours down his chin and wrists.

He looks at her and the veil slips off. He's right on the

edge, his size fully utilised. She recognises him now. Her dad sneers down at her and Annie plants her feet and exhales, ready. She has waited a long time for this.

And then it is over. Paul backs away, shaking his head. He wipes his face on his sleeve and apologises. Annie can see Nia running across the road, her curls bouncing behind her. Paul's blood has left a dark smear on the bonnet of his car.

No, Annie says, advancing.

She punches him. Her fist hits his cheekbone with a smooth crack like a nut. He doesn't fight back. For a second she wonders if he even knows how to fight.

Annie gets one more in, a backhanded slap that makes him gasp, before Nia pulls her off. Hot wind rushes past her face and she struggles, pulls away, needs to keep hitting him. She screams. Tells him over and over again that there is no forgiveness here. Her voice is ragged.

Paul just nods, his mouth still open, blood draining through the gaps between his teeth. Annie notes that to anyone passing by she looks like the villain. Nia tries to drag her out of the parking lot before the cafe staff can reach them.

Annie takes it all in: Paul wincing, avoiding her gaze. His own blood on his leathery hands. She pastes this image over every other one she has of him

Annie

2018, London

So Suri is gay. Annie stands alone in the middle of a crowded bar in Haggerston. There's a drag show on. The people here look good – bare skin and loud makeup. She leans against the wall, choking down her anger. Running her finger between her brows, kneading her face back into wary reserve, trying to merge into the queer joy around her.

Before dinner, Annie passed out on her uncle's couch and woke up as disoriented as she had been on the first night. She had missed calls from her mum and one from Monica. She deleted them all and texted Gran the link to a poem she had saved for her. Suri said his husband, Isaac Owusu, was returning from New York where he was consulting on a new restaurant, and would join them for dinner.

Annie had groaned. This is at least some of the explanation for Suri's beautiful life. She and Gran used to watch Isaac's cooking show every Thursday night. They would lie on opposite ends of the same couch, the soles of their feet touching. She wonders exactly how long Isaac has known about his niece on the other side of the world, watching him on the TV.

Annie didn't think she could handle meeting a tv personality on so little sleep, and left before Isaac got home. She has managed to commit, a little, to her look: blush, nice jeans, leather jacket. But she's underdressed. The girl opposite Annie is wearing pleasers.

A drag king with painted abs starts his show and while people swarm the stage, Annie pushes through to the bar. The bartender passes her a pint and the card machine without looking at her. She exhales properly for the first time since walking in. Being queer back home was claustrophobic: everyone knew everyone; everyone knew who everyone else had fucked.

Working in a bar like this could be good for her. Stunties have an expiry date; the injuries start mounting. The actresses Annie doubles for are often playing teenagers. The drag king jumps off stage and starts dancing on tables. Annie pictures Suri and Isaac at lavish dinners with their own queer friends. She needs to drink faster.

Can I get you another? He is sat at the bar next to Annie, his nose pierced twice on one side, pointing to her beer. He's looking at her through long eyelashes and smiling in a way that makes Annie want to press the cold pint to her neck. She nods before she can help herself.

His name is Ali. He taps his fingers on the bar too fast, like he is listening to a different soundtrack from everyone else. His friends stare at Annie without embarrassment, looking away only when the new act starts. One of them, with broad shoulders and sparkling lilac eyeshadow, smiles.

Ali tells her he is Lebanese and is relieved to hear she isn't South African. Annie asks if he thought she was white, and he takes a long sip of his beer before he answers.

I wasn't sure.

What do you know about New Zealand? she asks, her voice straining over the crowd's applause.

Good coffee. Bad cocaine.

A ruffled sleeve reaches out and taps Ali. He turns around and Annie takes the opportunity to retreat. She'd hoped that being in the sort of space she loved back home would be a comfort. But all these people with their friends just make her feel alone. She stands outside of the crowd, on edge.

The friend with the lilac eyeshadow finds her and says their name is Clove. They're light-skinned, maybe half like Annie. How long are you in town for then? they ask.

I'm not sure. I might look for a job. Maybe go travelling.

What's the queer scene like where you're from?

In Auckland? Annie says.

They nod.

Annie sighs, hesitates.

Is it that bad?

It's just small. After a few goes round there's nowhere to get off.

Clove smiles. About the same as here then.

I doubt that.

You'll see. There's only so many of us, once you learn who to avoid. We're all fucking in the same sandpit. Clove sips their drink through a metal straw.

Ali appears and Clove puts their arm around Annie's shoulder, before giving up their place with a giggle.

So why did you leave New Zealand? Ali asks.

To avoid my mother. Annie drains her pint.

The bar is dim in a way that seems intentional, but which hides dirt better than it creates a vibe. The counter they lean on, its edges carved with ornate curlicues, is sticky.

What did your mum do that was so bad? Ali asks.

Annie gestures to the bartender for another.

She kept me from my uncle.

Ali tells Annie he's trans before he fucks her. She tells him she hasn't had sex since her last big relationship and might cry. When she peels off her singlet he gives a happy shout. His skin tastes like mango body butter.

She knows she is partially here to forget about the pain of the last few days, but she is surprised when she actually does. Ali lights a joint that he fishes out from a drawer beside his bed and the tip glows like a little star in the dark. He tells

Annie he works for a comic book artist.

I'm his assistant, basically. I do editorial stuff, a bit of research. I thought it would help me break into the industry but I'm just his bitch.

Annie turns her face to Ali and breathes in his neck, the cologne that has blended with hers.

It's okay for now, he says. He passes her the joint.

Do you go to things like that often? Drag shows? she asks.

We go if we know someone. Sunday brunch is permanent though. He pauses. You could come, if you want?

Annie turns onto her back again and inhales, closing her eyes.

I like your life, she tells him.

She wakes in a panic.

The bedroom has no windows except for one on the ceiling. The sky on the other side is still dark. A vine with three-point leaves climbs up the side of the wall and curves around the skylight. Ali's clothes hang from uniform wooden hangers on a thick steel clothes rack, shoes lined up neatly underneath.

Annie pictures the two of them watching the sunrise, their bodies casting shadows on the leaf-covered wall, feels the sweet intoxication of starting a new relationship in a new country. She uses Ali's charger.

She can't believe that no one told her Suri is gay. That he's married. That he's stylish and kind. Annie might actually have liked her childhood if Suri was around.

What would it have been like to grow up with a brown man who cries and loves food and expensive dressing-gowns? They could have had some fun. They could have been a real family. He could have protected them. She came all this way because she was hopeful for the future, just to discover a new way to feel miserable about the past.

Annie has missed calls from Monica, her mum and Suri. None from Gran. She's furious about the time she wasted, that she didn't leave New Zealand the second she had money to spare. There has been so much life out here, expecting her.

Annie dials. She is energised by her rage.

Before her mum has a chance to say anything, Annie says, You knew how much I'd love him.

Annie. I've been trying to get hold of you.

Her voice is just the same, higher than Annie's and Gran's, with a sweetness to it even when she is upset. Ali stirs in his sleep and Annie lowers her voice, hissing into the phone.

Why did you keep him from me?

Her mum's sharp intake of breath.

Annie thumps the bed, knocks the tears off her cheeks with her fists. She pictures her mum sitting in her office at her messy desk, hair caressing her face, or curling away from the accusations spitting out of the phone.

Gran's had a stroke. I'm in Melbourne, she says, finally.

Annie sits up too fast and sees black specks darting around in her vision. Ali is wide awake now and staring at her.

Is she okay? What happened? Can I talk to her?

I think you should come.

Sithara

2018, Melbourne

Sithara got the call about Amma at the end of a long day. A stroke and a heart attack. She packed her laptop, the clothes that were closest, and left without socks or underwear, scared of missing the flight.

There are many chapters of Sithara's life she is still trying to understand. She used to wonder if she had a secret desire to be punished, if that was why she was unable to pull herself away from Paul. It was easier to believe she wanted to be treated badly.

On the plane she is unable to focus on any of the in-flight entertainment, too worried about the state she will find Amma in. Instead she scrolls through her phone. Annie stopped sending emojis around 2007. The x's at the end of her texts disappeared in 2009. There's a text in 2017 asking for Paul's number and a few days later she sent Sithara 'I love you'. Little black letters that felt like trumpets heralding a new age.

It was Nia who called Sithara and told her about Annie assaulting Paul. She explained the whole thing calmly, but when she hung up, Sithara knew she wouldn't be hearing from Nia again.

For a couple of weeks she wondered whether Paul would press charges. She was distressed by the ugliness of the incident, embarrassed by its implications. But the next time she went out running, her hair in two long plaits thumping against her shoulders, she thought about Annie fracturing Paul's nose and wondered where on earth she got the courage.

✦

Maude Aunty opens the door to Sithara, her lips pursed.

Now you come? she asks, one eyebrow raised. Sithara hangs her head. Maude grunts and takes her hand. She pulls her inside, back into a house filled with family.

They head straight to Amma's cottage without stopping. Sithara wheels her suitcase, mouth filling with spit.

Aunty, could I use the bathroom? she asks.

Maude points back to the house, to a blue-tiled room, and Sithara darts in, steadying herself on the side of the bath before she throws up into the toilet. She rinses her mouth without looking in the mirror, disgusted.

Sithara has wanted to die many times. This moment is different. This is just shame come to touch her face with its burning hands and she has withstood worse than this before. She calls Annie and it goes straight to voicemail. She waits a few minutes and dials again. Before Sithara leaves the bathroom she calls a third time and leaves a stuttering message telling her to call back, please.

Amma is held upright by a series of cushions and foam bolsters. She looks like all the youth has been scraped out of her, leaving deep crevices and hollows. Her head lolls to the side and one eye is open, focused on Sithara trembling in the doorway.

Maude readjusts Amma's head and brings a cup of water with a straw in it to her lips.

Sithara stares at the peonies. They stand in a glass vase on the bedside table next to Amma's curry plant. They were probably fine this morning, still a hint of blushing pink. But tonight they fill the room with the smell of rotting fish, faded petals unfolding like used napkins.

I called Annie, Sithara says.

Maude looks up at her. Amma's eyelid twitches.

And what about Suri? Maude asks. Sithara doesn't reply.

Maude gestures for Sithara to take a seat on the other side of Amma, between a flower and a person who are both dying. But Sithara skirts the bed and walks over to the window. Below her is a tidy vegetable garden: carrots, silverbeet, two different kinds of lettuce. Behind her, Amma's loud slurping and the scrape of Maude setting down the glass. Amma offers sounds, incoherent mutters.

241

What was that, Amma? Sithara turns, her hair reaching out to touch the edge of the bed frame. Amma makes more unintelligible sounds and Sithara looks at Maude, her voice breaking. Why can't Ammi talk?

Maude takes Sithara by the shoulders and pushes her firmly into the chair. Your cousin Vida is coming to take us through speech therapy. Stay with her. She glares at Sithara and leaves.

They are together, alone. There is nothing between them. Amma looks at Sithara with her one eye and motions with a hand to her own hair, her face. She passes a shaky finger over her eyebrows.

Sithara is an artist with tweezers these days. She can pull ingrown hairs without breaking the skin, clean her own brows up in barely any light. She brushes Amma's brows with a spoolie from her handbag so she can see what bits need tidying.

Sithara goes into Amma's ensuite and prepares, laying out tweezers, scissors, moisturiser, a comb, one wet flannel and another dry. She wipes Amma's face, sweeping down her neck and collarbone.

Her skin is slack. Her hair has thinned out and gone completely white. Sithara uses the scissors to trim them. She pulls the coarse white hairs out from the tails of her brows, the defiant dark ones from her upper lip. She can't help but admire the architecture of it all, Amma's cheekbones and her small pretty nose. Amma watches closely, one eye following Sithara as she tends to her.

Once done, she gently moisturises Amma's face and then runs the comb through her hair, setting her sparse curls back from her forehead.

Suri, Amma says, before Sithara's hands pull away.

Not wanting to seem as though she is unravelled by his name, Sithara looks down to hide her face, wipes errant tears from the corners of her eyes.

She places her hands on the bed, side by side with Amma's, wondering when one will morph into the other, if she will still remember the texture of Amma's hands when the rich brown of her own has wrinkled and faded.

✦

The speech therapist is a small white woman with silver rings trimming her ears and nose. She is as firm with Amma as she is with Sithara and Maude, explaining that whenever Amma is not resting or eating, someone must be running through vocal exercises with her.

After one session Amma is able to ask for Annie. She overcompensates first, opens her mouth too wide, her tongue pink and clumsy. She reacquires names slowly. After two days she can say short sentences. She throws her working hand up at the end to colour her words. Annie still won't answer Sithara's calls.

On the third day Sithara leaves Amma with Maude and ventures into Melbourne to buy toiletries. When she is heading home in the twilight, Annie finally calls back, full of righteous anger. Of course she went to Suri. She gave Sithara her plants, said no goodbye, and wore a look of grim resolution. Sithara knew she was leaving to find her uncle.

She thinks about Annie in London, both of them looking up into an unfamiliar sky.

Annie is older when she finally shows up at Maude's gate in her leather jacket. There are dark circles under her eyes. She is wary, entirely unfeminine, remarkably herself, as she has always been. Her phone buzzes incessantly, a signal she is wanted elsewhere. The hug is a surprise.

Sithara struggles not to bring him up. To ask what conversations Annie had with Suri, whether he listened better, spoke to her more kindly than Sithara can. She tries to flatten her sense of being betrayed when she leaves Annie with Amma and the two of them look peaceful.

Sithara wants in, desperately. Annie and Suri, Annie and Amma. She wants to tell them all that there is so much they don't know. She has kept her terrible years with Paul to herself, scared of being judged for what she was content to put up with. She has tried, hard, to convince herself that the person who loved him was an entirely different, separate Sithara.

But even though she became so small it was like she lived

in the corner of her own body, all of her was there – she was the one who picked Paul over Suri. And just before Annie finished high school, she folded, and picked him over Annie too. She told herself this is not how love works, that choosing to love someone can only ever bring people together, but she knew it was Annie or Paul.

When they reunited she burrowed into his adoration and for a moment she became young again, warmed by a creaking kind of happiness. But it was the second time around and Sithara was imitating herself. She was doing all the moves, but she couldn't hear any music. It was a new grief to realise there had never been any. That she was only ever dreaming up love, dancing to the sound in her own head. And when she woke up missing Annie like hell, she looked at Paul and her love was, finally, gone.

She yearns to explain herself. To tell Annie that loving someone for a very long time is always joy and devastation, that the existence of one doesn't disprove the other.

When Annie leaves Amma, Sithara takes her place. Annie has binned the peonies, cleaned the bedside table and refilled Amma's water. She has put away the pile of clean washing that was stacked in front of the window. It smells less like death than it did before. Amma is awake, waiting.

I'm sorry, she says. I'm sorry Paul hurt you and I couldn't stop it.

Sithara has not heard Amma apologise before, for anything. She takes a breath. Her first impulse is to pretend she doesn't need it. Instead she nods and rests her hand on Amma's shoulder.

Amma settles back into the pillows. Sithara checks the small notepad by the bed, where Maude has handwritten the medication Amma needs to take each day, the time and the amount. Annie has left small ticks beside her morning doses.

How strange that something as small as words can help. In the middle of all of her days now is this, this apology, like a seed. Yesterday was terrible, tomorrow will bring its own kind of pain, but if Sithara squints she can see the way ahead for the first time.

There is a shriek in the distance, inside the big house where Annie is showering and Maude is preparing dinner. Amma doesn't stir. Sithara holds her breath, waiting for another sound, for a revelation.

There it is again, smaller, brighter, more like a cheer than a scream. Sithara jumps. Her hair is pulsing, full of an energy so big it hums. She runs out of the cottage, crosses the small garden in two steps and reaches the glass doors, throwing them open and letting everything, everything in.

Suri.

He is old now, which means she is too. He looks at her and she knows who he sees. The only reason her hair has ever mattered to her is the same reason it matters now to Suri, because it is so like Appa's. Sithara sees Suri's twelve-year-old face in the mirror, brushing his teeth beside her.

She remembers arriving in Invercargill, being cold to her bones and holding his dimpled hand on the street.

He is entirely bald now and his head is shining. Isaac Owusu is standing at his side, which strikes her as odd.

Annah, Sithara says. Suri's skin and hands and eyes are her own.

She steps close and touches his shoulders, too nervous to hug him properly.

She wants to tell him that everything is still here. That the room is exactly as he left it this time, because when he moved away she boarded up the door. And then his bottom lip quivers and all she can get out is three words, whispered.

I missed you.

Annie
2018, Melbourne

Gran is fast asleep. Her hands are folded over her stomach. Her feet lie in a patch of sunlight. They are as small as a child's. It isn't the same bed she had when Annie left. This one has a remote control sitting in its own cloth pocket and a big red emergency button hanging by her head.

Annie rushes closer but her mum stops her.

She had the stroke the day you left. It was random, it could have happened anytime. The hospital put her in an induced coma for twelve hours and discovered she had a very small heart attack as well.

Mum speaks soft and slow, like she is trying hard to convince Annie that things are okay. Gran's hair looks thin. Annie's heart is beating fast, her ears ringing.

Your gran has all her mental faculties, she's exactly the same person. But she's a bit more emotional than you'll be used to, and she's sleepy. You can talk to her just like you always do. There's no need to be scared.

I could never be scared of Gran.

Her mum gives her a tight smile. It feels like a failure of their relationship that her mum is too nervous to ask her about Suri.

The sheets crunch a little under Annie's hands, like there is plastic below them. She presses her face to Gran's, but feels tears slipping down her cheeks. She pulls away before she wakes Gran by dripping on her. Without opening her eyes, Gran's hand finds Annie's.

Annie, Gran says.

She slurs. Her voice is ragged. The left side of her face droops like there is a thread pulling her chin and her cheeks down.

Annie climbs on the bed next to her.

It's okay, she whispers. Everything's going to be okay.

Gran shakes her head. Her neck trembles. Her shame climbs the walls like a vine.

Annie looks at her tightly closed eyes, the hyperpigmentation scattered across her face. I love you, Gran, her voice clear as rain.

Gran presses a hand to the air as though telling Annie to pause. Pātti was the only person who loved me, she says, her words blurring together. And she was too old to take care of me.

Annie slows her breathing. She has never once been told about Gran's childhood.

They tried to give me away, Gran says. They sold me to a rich man who had a son. The son was supposed to marry me.

What is pouring out sounds ancient, older than Gran herself.

Gran's neck stops shaking. She opens her eyes and looks straight at Annie. Her irises are light brown flecked with gold. She raises her head and starts to talk.

✦

Annie unhooks her mind in the shower. It's the only place she is able to imagine different spaces, different lives. It's where she realised she was queer, where she wonders if she is cruel to her mum, where she understood they would never really be complete without Suri.

Today she imagines Gran in old Singapore. She doesn't know what that life would look or feel like, but she tries to let it seep into her, the feeling of being ten years old and at a dead end. She lifts up pieces of her hair so she can rub shampoo right onto her scalp, and wishes she could time travel.

Gran killed her rapist. Somehow this is not new; it is like a song Annie is listening to decades later, remembering all of the lyrics. Gran killed her rapist because of course she did. Annie sees the three of them – Gran, Mum and herself – swimming in the same dark water. They don't cross paths, they just stay side by side, keeping their eyes locked on one another.

Shampoo runs white trails down her shoulders. Sadness anchors her. Annie wrings her hair like a rag and steps out. She dries herself off in a hurry, assessing her face in the mirror, judging the symmetry of her lips, the angle of her chin. Scrutinising her large nose and heavy brows, which are really the only things that make her look South Asian.

She pulls nail scissors from the cupboard behind the mirror and snips a piece of her hair close to the root. It sticks straight up in the middle of her head like an antenna. The scissors are too small to do anything useful, so Annie shuffles cleansers and bottles of castor oil around until she finds what she is looking for.

The clean blade of the clippers against her head is as warm and soothing as the shower. Strands of hair fall around her shoulders like cut weeds. She leaves less than an inch in her wake and the stubble is glossy. She drags the clippers two, three times across the top.

She manages to get the kitchen scissors out of the drawer without bumping into anyone and rushes back to the bathroom.

There is a shriek. Coming from the hallway. It cuts through the house. Annie opens the bathroom window and tips out far enough to see the entranceway. Two people are standing there. She recognises the top of Suri's head. He looks behind, perhaps checking to see if it is too late to turn back.

Annie feels her mum coming from Gran's cottage

before she sees her, and she walks down the stairs to the entranceway as though she is on set, watching herself on the monitor and remembering every single thing.

Suri must have caught the very next flight after hers. He looks so nervous, standing here, hands by his side like he doesn't know what to do with them.

Annie tries to cover her bald strip with her hands before Isaac can see it. She's used to working with famous people, but she's never been related to one. He's short in person, knitted wool beanie and hipster-ish tattoos. He looks uncomfortable to be here and watches Suri with concern.

Her mum and Suri embrace. They are tentative at first. And then her mum squeezes Suri tight and his head rests on her shoulder and Annie feels the air around all of them shift, rise, and settle.

The emergency alarm buzzes through the house. Maude gets a fright and Isaac moves forward to steady her. Her mum takes Suri's hand and walks him straight towards Gran's house. Annie hovers, she feels responsible for the shiny stranger that has appeared in their house next to Suri. But Isaac and Maude start talking like they know one another.

Gran has angled the head of her bed so that it pushes her up. She holds the blanket to her chin with her working hand. One shoulder is exposed, blouse trailing off a shoulder blade that is sharp like the scissors. Her good hand is on the emergency buzzer and she is watching the door expectantly when they all burst in.

Her lips go tight when she sees Suri. He stands steadfast in the doorway, but he looks at his sister for a cue. Her hair is tucked behind her ears; it is completely still. Annie has never seen her look so unsure. Gran's good eye is slowly moving over the array of people in front of her.

None of them thought of a second step. In front of Gran they are all children. Annie feels embarrassed. They are floundering, the air thick with all the things they cannot say.

Then Gran clocks Annie's strange appearance and her jaw drops. She starts to shake. Annie goes to soothe her. Her mum pulls out her phone and calls Vida, her voice frightened.

What did you do? Gran says.

Annie opens her mouth and closes it again, unsure how to explain. Suri puts a hand out in front of Annie like he is trying to deflect Gran's rage.

But Gran and Annie start laughing.

Annie's laugh is an open-mouthed roar that doubles the size of her head. Gran's is throaty and soft. Her mum clutches the bed with one hand and flutters between the two of them. It is bewildering how close belly-shaking mirth sits to grief. She feels herself shift out of sadness so fast she wonders if the two feelings are somehow one.

When the laughter dies down, her mum sits Annie on a chair at the end of Gran's bed with a towel around her shoulders and finishes cutting her hair. Gran stays upright but closes her eyes. She hasn't eaten today. Annie tried to feed her the thin runny porridge she always eats, but she rubbed her stomach and made a face.

Suri and Gran still haven't said a word to one another. Annie waits, listening to the whisper of scissors around her shoulders and the rattle of Gran's breath. Her mum stands back and Suri takes over with the clippers. He cups his hands on the back of Annie's head and starts to shave.

The skin around Gran's elbows has folded and sagged. She tips off balance even in the bed, all her weight leaning towards the side of her body that continues to respond to what her brain tells it. Her lips are still dusky pink like tea roses.

Amma had long hair once, Mum says.

Gran opens an eye.

It was never like yours, or Ravi's. She gestures around herself. It was just hair.

Suri murmurs cautiously, agreeing.

He places the clippers on top of Gran's drawers and Annie rubs her hand slowly over her head. She has never felt air against her scalp before. Her palm comes away with tiny pieces of hair stuck to it.

Gran, do you remember me telling you that I had a breakup? she says.

Suri looks at her with a frown.

I didn't know how to say it at the time, but the breakup was with a woman. Her name was Nia. I thought she was the love of my life. Maybe she is.

Suri's hands start to shake. Her mum looks to the door as though checking the way is clear for escape. But Annie is light, like she's levitating. She wants to take Gran along, make both of them weightless.

I wanted to tell you. I thought about it. But every time I tried, I felt sick. I think I was scared you wouldn't love me anymore.

Gran studies her. She doesn't look mad, or even especially shocked. Her eye flicks to Sithara, to Suri, and back to Annie. She grunts. Anyway, you look the part, now, she says.

Suri chokes on what sounds like a sob and coughs to cover it.

Gran closes her eye and tips her head back on her pillows, angelic.

Annie stands alone in her cousin Keshani's bedroom. Keshani is at university in Sydney, but someone has made the bed with clean sheets.

Now it is just Annie and her bald head in front of the mirror. She runs her hand over it and is relieved not to feel any bumps or indentations. In fact, her head is perfectly round, like a ball. Her ears are really in their element now. She doesn't look so bad.

Annie goes to the bed and opens her suitcase. She empties it, separates what is dirty and what she will wear tomorrow. She lifts out her yoga mat so she can stretch before she finally sleeps. And then she repacks, feeling her mind and body relax.

Her mum knocks on the open door.

It suits you.

I might go to a barber to get the edges fixed.

Her own hair is waving gently again. Annie stares at it in the mirror and wonders why she has always taken her mum's hair for granted.

Appa, your grandfather Ravi, she says, as though this is an explanation. He had hair like mine. You could look at it and see exactly what he was thinking. She falters, heartbreak bleeding into the room.

It has always been like this when her mum tries to talk about him.

I'm sorry I didn't give you a dad like that.

Annie tries to think of something to say in return. That her anger about Paul has shifted, shrunk. That it's waning more and more every day, that it no longer feels like headlights thundering towards them both. That she doesn't blame her. But even though she's not angry like she was, she is still unsure.

It is so much easier to talk to Suri than her mum. There are no debts to settle, no resentment.

I love him, Annie says. I did straightaway. I wish you had told me about him.

Her mum's face changes and Annie sees that she has hurt her. But she doesn't apologise, or take it back. Her mum nods and turns to go, hair trailing the wall behind her as she leaves, like there is more to say.

✦

What did your achi say, huh? Maude asks.

She lays takeaway menus from a Sri Lankan restaurant out on the counter. Annie looks through the windows into Gran's cottage. The lights are off but she can feel Gran's eyes blazing in the dark.

She told me I looked like a dyke, Annie says.

Isaac comes in wearing fresh clothes, shaking his head like he overheard. Maude offers them a drink, and he and Annie both choose beer.

It's so good to finally meet you Aunty, Isaac says.

You two know each other? Annie asks.

We write, don't we? Isaac sits down next to Annie.

We've all hoped this would happen, darling, Maude says.

Annie thinks about Suri leaving the kitchen to phone Isaac. His weary resignation. So Annie was only the catalyst, clumsy and reckless.

You gave Gran their address, didn't you? Annie asks Maude.

Maude just pats her on the head.

Annie looks over the menus. She isn't sure what a lot of the food is. She realised only recently that the meals Gran used to cook had names other than the ones Annie gave them as a child. 'Noodle pancakes' are string hoppers, or idiyappam. 'Buns' are maalu paan. 'Salad' is raita.

Maude's eyes light up when Suri comes in. She asks only Suri what he wants for dinner and silences his pleas to wait for Sithara before calling to order. She sits beside him, locking her arm through his. The conversation halts. Gran's cottage feels like it is sliding closer, the garden between them disappearing.

Suri shreds one of the menus in his fingers. Maude Aunty looks like a raven. Her eyes are black as poppyseeds and her head trembles on her neck.

A light comes on in the cottage. Annie closes her eyes and listens with her body like she did as a child. Her mum isn't upstairs anymore. She must be over with Gran, getting her ready. Maude Aunty gets up and starts laying plates and napkins on the table. Isaac fills a jug of water and puts out glasses, despite Maude insisting he sit back down.

Annie texts Ali. He responds immediately and sends back fire emojis when she tells him she has shaved her head. Isaac sees the way she is smiling at her phone.

You met someone in London? he asks.

Annie just shrugs, nervous to get the full force of his attention.

The cottage door opens and her mum pushes Gran across the grass in a wheelchair. Suri stays sitting at the table, staring at the pile of ripped paper in front of him. Gran is wrapped in blankets – one across her lap and one behind her, softening the imprint of the wheelchair against her body. Black wool with red and orange lines. Annie can't decide whether Gran looks regal or like she is going into battle.

The doorbell rings and Annie sees an escape. When she returns with the food, Gran is seated at one end of the table, Maude opposite. Her mum is on one side of Gran and the seat on her other shoulder is free for Annie. Isaac and Suri are ensconced safely on either side of Maude.

As Annie opens lids, Maude announces their contents: kottu roti vegetarian, pumpkin curry, bitter gourd, black pork curry, crab, prawns, egg appam.

Annie starts helping herself to the pork and Maude takes the spoon out of her hands.

That one's meat, darling.

Yes, Annie says.

You eat meat? Suri asks. Maude and Isaac are both looking at her.

Yes.

Suri blinks. We just assumed you were a vegetarian.

No, just a queer, she says. Annie fills her plate and passes the pork to Suri.

He's allergic, Isaac and Gran say at the same time.

Suri looks right at Gran. Her head barely clears the table. Her working hand sits on the side of her plate, the unresponsive one tucked out of view. She looks back at Suri, gives him a tiny shake of the head as if to say hello and smiles her crooked smile.

Suri stands up quickly. His hands make fists at his side. He looks out beyond the table, beyond the garden, beyond the little plot of land his mother has made a home on. He screws up his face like he is holding back the flood.

Annie tries to imagine all of the things he is feeling. She told Gran she was gay, just like Suri, but paid nothing for it.

He reaches over and makes Gran's plate, putting small spoonfuls of each dish in a circle around her rice, pouring thick red chilli sauce on the side, the kind Annie used to watch Gran drown BBQ pork buns in. Before Suri sits back down, he pushes the plate close enough for Gran to eat without spilling.

Mum has tied her hair in a rare ponytail. She's eating with her hand, adding extra mango pickle to the side of her plate with a spoon. Suri tells Maude Aunty about the three restaurants he and Isaac own. He dabs his forehead with a napkin and points to the pumpkin, nodding at Isaac.

Annie tries to study Isaac without him noticing. She resents him. Not for being here, for witnessing these dysfunctional and revealing family moments, but for being with Suri. Annie wants her uncle all to herself.

Isaac half-listens to Suri, his eyes keep darting back to Gran. Annie has learned to be wary of famous people, to tread the balance between acknowledging status without admiring it. In her experience, celebrities both expect civilians to be impressed by them, and act repulsed when it actually happens. Isaac notices Annie staring and asks how her food is. She gives a thumbs-up and promises herself she will never tell him how good he was on TV.

Maude Aunty stares at Gran, pushing her own food around her plate without actually eating any. Gran slides only small bits of rice into her mouth. But she sucks noisily on the pork bone, wrapping her lips around it and pulling the meat back with her teeth, leaving the blackened bone white. She has always eaten with her lips smacking, her eyes creasing with satisfaction when something is truly good. She used to cook Annie crab curry and crack the claws with a mallet, dragging the meat out with her fingers and dropping it onto Annie's plate. She would pour the curry sauce on top so that every mouthful Annie took would be just right. She has cooked and fed Annie so many of her own favourite foods that Annie doesn't know if she's ever had any tastes that didn't belong to Gran first.

Isaac clears his throat. I wish I could get my husband to cook like this for me.

I never taught him, Gran says, shrugging.

Amma used to throw us out if we came in when she was making food, her mum says.

Akki, she used to *banish* us, Suri says.

What is Akki? Annie asks Suri.

Older sister, Maude Aunty says. This one calls me Akki too. She waves her spoon at Gran.

Gran wipes the side of her mouth with a napkin and presses it to her forehead.

Ammi? Suri says.

Shall we go back? her mum asks.

Gran nods and holds out her hand for Annie. Suri gets up and goes to her wheelchair.

The four of them make their way to Gran's cottage in the dark, rocking over the paving stones, tucking Gran's blankets in tighter to protect her from the drop in temperature that happens here as soon as the sun goes down.

This moment – her mum, Suri and Gran all together – feels to Annie like everything she's ever wanted.

Her mum takes Gran to her ensuite to help her get ready for bed, Suri heads back to the big house and Annie is left alone in the middle of the bedroom. She closes the curtain and dims the light. There is a length of batik cloth over Gran's duvet that Annie remembers from long, long ago. She can't place where. Perhaps a tablecloth. The room smells precisely of Gran: mothballs, faint incense and rose hand cream.

Annie's phone buzzes, but rather than clear her messages she turns it off.

She makes a pot of tea in the small kitchen and sets cups on the bench, adding three sugars to her mum's and to Gran's. She's not sure how many to add to Suri's so she gives him three as well. Then she presses her hands over her eyes.

Suri finds her crying by the teapot.

Don't you feel like we wasted so much time? she asks him. Doesn't it feel awful?

Suri considers her. He looks tired.

It used to. I was so angry, Annie, for so long.

Annie wipes her eyes.

You're brave for telling her like that, Suri says.

Annie laughs so she doesn't cry again.

He leans on the bench beside her. I told her after this white boy kissed me, he says. All the girls at school had a crush on him, so it felt like a badge of honour. It gave me confidence.

What was his name?

Fraser Duncan. Very pretty, great hair.

How old were you?

Suri stares into his tea for a long time before he responds.

I was eighteen. It seems young to me now. He stops talking. Annie waits.

There was one time that I really should have told her, and I couldn't. There was a boy who worked in our house. His name was Jayaraj, but everyone called him Chintu. He was the first boy I ever loved. We were just kids, and we lived together, so of course we experimented. But we were reckless and we got caught. In a way, that was my coming out.

He looks so sad that she reaches out and puts her hand over his.

I didn't know how much danger I was putting him in until it was too late.

Her mum comes in distressed, telling Suri she needs help.

Annie watches Suri zip up his grief and follow his sister out the door. She considers that less than a week ago she didn't know if her uncle would want to speak to her at all.

Josephina
2018, Melbourne

Josephina is awake for only a moment before the sun goes out.

She went to sleep happy, this she knows, but she blinks open and everything is dark as twilight. There are a few seconds of pain. And then her whole body starts to freeze and burn at the same time.

She must have shouted, because they come running. Sithara cradles her head and Maude speaks into a phone, saying it is worse than the first. Her words hang in the air without taking shape and Josephina wonders if she will die the same way Ravi did. With her head in the arms of someone who loves her.

Josephina wakes up in hospital, Annie and Suri by her side. She still can't see out of her left eye and now the right is blurry too. There are deep moans from the bed beside her. Moans that creak like footsteps, shadows moving across laminated floors. She is so tired. She reaches for Annie's cool hand and holds it while the doctor examines her.

The doctor asks if Josephina wants to be resuscitated if it happens again. She tries to tell Annie to go and get the others but the words that come out of her mouth are slow and they hurt to listen to. She sounds like an idiot. Annie understands enough and leaves. Josephina jabs her finger at one side of the clipboard and the doctor circles 'DNR'.

Suri reaches out instead, his hand enveloping hers. Her small boy has come home, glowing. His life just as bright and as big as Ravi hoped it would be.

And then time slows. She closes her eyes and listens to the parrots in the trees outside.

Vida comes in when her shift finishes, harried and blunt, still in work mode. She tries to convince Josephina to stay in the hospital. But Josephina has no trouble bending her expectations of life to fit into the length of time offered to her.

After seeing others her own age die slowly, she has grown envious of Ravi's simple exit. Those left behind to wither away, missing their lovers, are not so lucky. She does still wonder whether she is damned for what she did as a child. But all that is long past now. No, she is entirely too old to languish in a sterile room, delaying the inevitable by bargaining endlessly with God. She makes Suri and Vida promise not to tell the others.

On their way home, the children and Annie in a separate

cab, Josephina asks Maude to stop the taxi by a park. She is lowered out onto her wheelchair and Maude pays the driver to wait. Then she wheels Josephina to a bench in the centre of the grass and they sit, side by side, feeling the sun on their faces.

Maude turns to her. My darling sister.

Josephina doesn't reply. She no longer trusts her voice to be a conduit for her feelings. Instead she turns her whole head so she can look directly at Maude. Josephina can see the old woman she has become and the young woman she used to be, and both of them arrive at the same time, like a blessing, when Maude smiles at her.

Josephina has so many regrets. Staying in Invercargill instead of heading back to Colombo for Nisha's funeral when she died only a year after Ravi. Destroying little Chintu and throwing him to the wolves. Most of all, Suri. Everything she did out of fear and shame that drove her son away.

Freed from expectation or a desire to live, Josephina's thoughts roam free. When the parrots go to roost, she is young again. She is on her bike, next to Mavis, rocketing through the streets of Singapore. Mavis's little head bobs up and down and she shouts at Josephina to hurry. The bike Mavis rides is green. She did extra babysitting for weeks before she got it.

Josephina sees herself in a tuktuk with Jing, helping her carry groceries into the small house where her daughter

Trinity is waiting with dinner ready. It is so good to see her old friends again. She calls out, trying to get them to turn and greet her, to see her as she is now, lined face and white hair.

Back at Maude's, Sithara fusses, cleaning aggressively. Suri reads the newspaper aloud to her. Annie and Isaac come in with plates of food Josephina does not want to eat. She closes her eyes to see herself in a crisp new sari, walking along a concrete road towards her first day teaching at Mount Lavinia. She stops and tucks her hair behind her ears. She checks there is no one watching and then touches her armpits to feel for perspiration. She looks like a bird of paradise.

Finally, after so many nights without him, she sees Ravi's face. First, he is a child, climbing with his brothers to cut down coconuts. He looks just like Sithara, skinny, with hair his mother has let grow too long out of love for the sheer beauty of it.

She sees him with his own father. They are sitting side by side at a dining table, laughing. Thehan Fernando has silver sideburns and he puffs away on a pipe.

Ravi is always smiling in her dreams. It is a joy to fall asleep and see his face in her mind's eye again. She feels as though he is drawing nearer, the gap between the two of them closing.

She sees Sithara the day she was born. With heavy-lidded eyes that still manage to catch Josephina's own and study her. Eyes that look up at Josephina with a message from a world beyond this one.

Josephina finds herself in the bathroom of their old house in Changi, looking at Pātti. Pātti cleans the point of her mighty widow's peak with one swipe of a razor blade and stares back at Josephina in the mirror.

She sees herself standing – rod-straight as though electrocuted – in her own kitchen, breathing shallow, listening to the fight erupting on the other side of the garden in Hamilton. She watches the front door of the big house open and Annie burst out, climbing into Josephina's own bed hours before bedtime.

She sees her younger self sneaking out when it is dark and Annie is asleep, picking her way over the damp grass under a full moon, standing outside and looking into the lounge where Paul is alone watching TV as though nothing at all had happened. Tapping the blade of a kitchen knife on the window. Tap, tap, tap, she pushes her nose right up to the glass and shakes her head at him and he stares back, pinned.

She dreams of one of the few times she tried, one of the many times she failed, to reconcile with Suri. She and Suri sit in an Indian restaurant in Dunedin, waiting for Sithara to join them. Neither of them try to make conversation. Her lips are curled in an expression of distaste. It stings to see the full effect of herself. Suri stares out the window like he wants to crash through it. More than anything else, this memory hurts.

And then her dreams circle back around and she is a child once more and brave, crouched, panting, on the windowsill of the good room. It lasts only a second; pain pulls her out. Her head throbs and she hears Annie's voice saying *Granny*. When she looks into Annie's eyes, there they all are, everyone she has ever loved.

Annie
2019, Colombo

Annie wakes up at 5 am. It's been like this since she and her mum arrived in Sri Lanka. Rather than try to work herself into a schedule that allows her to sleep in, she has accepted it. Each morning that greets her here is brighter than the one before.

Annie thinks she looks better in Colombo. Her skin is so clear. When she stretches, her body bends like her joints have been oiled. Her hair has grown back curly. At first it was soft like baby's hair and she thought it would be temporary. But as it got longer, the curls became tighter. She keeps it short. Annie is trying to learn how to touch her own hair again.

The city dawns grey and purple. They are staying in an Airbnb in Colombo, close to the ocean and a train station. Trees and plants thrive on the edges of apartment buildings and the pollution hanging in the air makes everything soft-focus. Annie stands at windows fitted with wooden slats, breathing the salt air in.

For the last half-hour of the plane ride she wept, wishing that Gran was with them. Annie didn't expect to feel like she was home when they landed. And she doesn't, not exactly. But there is a feeling of recognition. In the thick eyelashes of the immigration officer who checked Annie's visa. In the fine wrists of the tuktuk driver who took them to their apartment. In the way that Sri Lankans hear 'Fernando' and nod like it is as common as 'Smith'. It is such a tender joy to realise that something inside her has always known what it is like to be *of* a place.

Annie can't remember her mum ever taking a holiday, but here she sleeps until noon. They are in Colombo for a week total. In three days they will take the train to Kandy where Suri and Isaac will be waiting. Then all five of them will travel to the coastal beaches. Suri wants to teach them to surf. Her mum isn't much of a swimmer. Annie can already surf. They are on a family holiday and they are going to go to the beach.

Her mum walks into the kitchen and fills the kettle.

What are you doing up? Annie asks.

I decided I should try to have at least one full day while we're here.

Her mum started wearing her hair in a long plait after Gran died. It makes her look so different, innocent. She brings Annie tea and the two of them stand side by side in the kitchen window, watching a crowded train pull away from a station painted pink.

Annie thinks about her Gran's confession and wonders whether she is the only one who knows. She hopes that what she said in return was not inadequate. That it helped.

She wishes she could have given Gran more. Assured her of something. Convinced her of everything. Played her a movie that would have helped her see that Annie's life only matters because of her, that it is because of Gran that Annie is complicated and familiar with rage and sure of herself.

Annie has all the words now she needed a year ago. The words to tell Gran she would have done the same thing herself a thousand times over. That blood for blood may not be the Christian way of going about things, but no price can be put on the innocence of a small child anyway.

But she knows even these words would not have been enough. Annie needed songs, books, paintings. She needed a tapestry with Gran's likeness woven into it, made from pieces of Annie's cast-away hair, or from a thousand multicoloured petals split into fine threads, so that the colours of Gran's face and eyes could be coloured as brightly as they were in life.

When the end was close, Annie did the only thing she could do. She held Gran's face in her hand and kissed both of her cheeks and thanked her. She told her she meant everything.

Gran held Annie's shoulder tight. She released her slowly like she was letting a small fish back into the sea. When Annie stood up, Suri took her place. The last time Annie saw Gran still alive, the happiness in her face was whole like an unbroken circle.

Grief is always close. It doesn't ask much of her, all things considered. Sometimes it asks that she remove herself from the picture, that she remembers her mum and Suri are dealing with a kind of loss that is harder to live with. Sometimes grief forces Annie to actually talk about her feelings and accept the parts of herself that seem weak and pathetic, the parts she has tried to carve out. She knows she is lucky to have a grief that is clean.

Still, she doesn't like the world as much without Gran in it. She wonders if she died with any other secrets.

Her mum goes to her half-unpacked suitcase and pulls out a pamphlet. The paper is glossy and there is a photo of the corner of a pearl-coloured building surrounded by grass.

National Museum of Colombo, Annie reads.

Her mum opens the pamphlet and points to the photograph of a huge tree with vines spiralling down like ribbons.

I thought we could go there today.

Sure, I like museums, says Annie.

Her mum shakes her head. Not the museum.

She looks again. You want to take me to the tree? Annie asks.

Her mum is staring at the water, arms crossed over her chest. Her own hair ebbs, endless as the sea itself.

It's where Amma and Appa met.

Annie looks at the tree again, trying to peel it off the paper and paint her grandparents onto the grass, underneath a ceiling of leaves.

That's so romantic.

Her mum turns to Annie. She is barefoot, with sleep still in the corners of her eyes. There's a good twist too, she says.

Annie tips forward to listen closer, she feels like she is about to receive impeccable gossip.

Another man. He spent his life pining for Amma.

Of course he did. Annie reaches out, stepping into arms that are thin like memory and hard like love. She feels as though she is at the edge of a dark forest teeming with life.

Acknowledgements

I could not have written a book without the support and love of my friends, family and teachers. I didn't know I could do this when I started, they showed me that I could.

Paula Morris, who has championed me as a writer and this work as a book before I could conceive of either. Thank you so much for believing that I could do this.

Abby Aitcheson, I still can't believe you were kind enough to take the time to read the first draft of a novel by someone you really didn't know. You were my first reader really, and your words were invaluable. Patricia Bell, I lucked out when I found you, what an incredible match of taste and sensibility.

Rosetta and James Allan, thank you for awarding the Crystal Arts Trust Prize to me, and thank you for creating it to sustain and encourage writers in the first place.

Rosabel Tan, you do so much to make the community around you better, and I am thrilled and endlessly grateful to be in your life. Thank you for seeing me, for always taking my work seri- ously and for believing in it. You and Leah have given the Slow Currents so much.

My literary agent, Angelique Tran Van Sang, I am so happy you read beyond my embarrassingly brief synopsis when I slid into your submissions. I like you as a person as much as I admire you as an editor and an agent. Thank you for your mind, your patience and your humour.

Kate Stephenson, thank you for guiding me through all of this. I felt immediately sure that we would have a great time working together and look I was right! I have learned so much about writing through working with you, Lamorna and Neil.

Lamorna Ash, thank you for your attention and for your incredible notes, you made it so easy to see the book differently. Neil Griffiths, thank you for your certainty about what the book needs. It has become so much better.

Jess Bourke, thank you for being so sure that this would all work out. Your responses to every new level I unlocked in the creation of this gave me so much confidence, and the way you approach your own career has inspired the dedication I now apply to my own. Thank you for your patience with me.

My friends who physically and emotionally sustained me over the years it took to write this, Kainee, Pratiksha, Julie, Zoë, Amy, Seb (boy), I love you, you make my life worth living. I could not have worked like this if I didn't have all of you to make me laugh throughout it. Bree, Seb (girl), and Emz, thank you for holding me so tight at the exact moment everything around me crumbled. Nisha, you have been a mentor to me before you even knew I existed, and now you're my friend, and still a guiding light for how to always keep what really matters at the forefront of the work.

Sophie McBride. You are just a total gift to me, I can't believe I get to know you. I'm so grateful every day that I get to have fun with, love you and be loved by you. You and me forever.

Karenza and Doug, there is just no way this book would have happened without the two of you putting me up while I wrote it. Dougie, thank you for being so hype about this book that you tell your patients about it. Mumma, a rewarding and essential part of growing up for me has been understanding more of you. I hope I can always use this understanding to be a better daughter. Thank you for caring for me and baking for me and for always being interested and invested in me. I love you so much.

Sisi, I love you, I hope you find something in here that matters. Thank you for always turning towards me even when I have turned away.

Granny, I didn't know where to put my grief when you died. It was too much for me, it was too much for the people around me. It was too much to live with, so I wrote you a book. I wish I could have known you at every age, this is my attempt to. Thank you for teaching me about art, for cooking for me, for sharing with me, for listening to me, for always always reading to me. Thank you for taking care of me when I couldn't take care of myself. Thank you for showing me bravery, for teaching me who to trust and how.

When I am in Wellington I still stand on your street and listen for you.

I'm excited to see you again in the next life, there is so much to talk about.

AMMA

SARAID DE SILVA

First published in 2024
by Weatherglass Books

Copyright © 2024 Saraid de Silva

A CIP record for this book is published by the British Library

ISBN: 978-1-7392601-4-9

Cover design: Luke Bird
Typesetting: James Tookey

Printed in the U.K. by TJ Books, Padstow

www.weatherglassbooks.com

Weatherglass
Books